THE EMERGENCY BOOK

all illustrated
by the author

THE
EMERGENCY
BOOK *Written and illustrated*

by **JEANNE BENDICK**

RAND McNALLY & COMPANY

CONTENTS

HV
675.5
B4

INTRODUCTION

It's a good idea to read this book through, at least once. Of course you'll know some of the things in it, but there will be a number of things you don't know, and maybe one of those could save you a lot of trouble, or even your life, in an emergency.

You certainly won't remember everything in the book from just reading through it, but your mind is the best computer in the world, with a memory bank better than any computer has. In an emergency, the facts you need, even if you don't think you remember them, can come popping out at you.

Mainly, though, this is a reference book. When you have an emergency, or a possible emergency is on the way, or when you are going into an unfamiliar situation, read through the section that applies. The fastest way to find your emergency, or your might-be-emergency, is by looking in the index at the back of the book.

Even if you learned everything in this book, there's a lot more to know. When you can, it's a good idea to take a First Aid course, a Water Safety or Life Saving course, and a Driver Education course before you start to drive. The more you know, the better prepared you are for any crisis—or adventure—you may meet.

WHAT WOULD YOU DO *IF* . . .?

Life is full of emergencies.

An emergency is an unexpected situation that calls for quick thinking. Usually an emergency happens suddenly. Often an emergency means danger, for you or somebody else. There are big emergencies, such as a fire in the house or falling through the ice when you're skating. There are little emergencies, such as blowing a fuse or getting locked out.

In an emergency, there's usually a right thing to do and a wrong thing to do. Knowing a few emergency rules will help you to make up your mind quickly.

1. KEEP CALM. Keep your head on your shoulders. You can't think clearly when you get into a panic, big or small, and clear thinking is important in any emergency.

Keep your head on your shoulders!

2. USE YOUR COMMON SENSE. Use whatever you know to help you out. But don't do *more* than you know how to do, especially in medical emergencies.

3. DO ONE THING AT A TIME. Think what to do next, one thing at a time, in a logical order. Then do each thing before you do the next thing. Take one step at a time if you are in a dangerous place. Help one person at a time if you're a rescuer.

4. REMEMBER THAT PEOPLE ARE MORE IMPORTANT THAN THINGS. Never put yourself, or anyone else, in danger to save a *thing*, even a thing as big as a house.

PREVENTING EMERGENCIES

Some emergencies can't be helped.

No one can prevent a hurricane or a flood or some other natural disaster. Some man-made emergencies can't be avoided either. You could call them fate — the wrong things coming together at the wrong time.

But many emergencies never should happen.

Most fires are caused by somebody's carelessness.

Most accidents happen because people are careless, or lazy, or just aren't thinking.

Any day, if you look around, you can see emergencies in the making:
A frayed electric wire;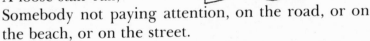
A loose stair rail;
Somebody not paying attention, on the road, or on the beach, or on the street.

In each section of this book there is a check list of things you can do to prevent emergencies. Use these check lists to take stock of your own apartment or house, and the way you do things.

HELP IN AN EMERGENCY

Every home should have a list of emergency telephone numbers, in plain sight, next to the telephone. They can be on the cover of the telephone book, or pasted on a card, or framed and hung next to the telephone.
These numbers should include:

The fire department;
The police department;
The doctor;
The nearest emergency hospital;
The nearest Poison Emergency Center, even if it's in another city;
Where everybody in the family can usually be reached when they are not at home;
Your nearest neighbors.

Keep the list up to date.

In an emergency, if you need help, ask for it. A good loud scream or repeated shouting is one of the best help-getters there is. Most people want to help if they know you need it.

There are many ways to ask for help, depending on the situation and where you are.

Just picking up the phone can get you help.

If you're at home and there's a fire or a prowler or a medical emergency, just pick up the telephone, get the operator and say:

"Please call the fire department," or

"Please get the police," or

"Please send an ambulance."

When the operator answers, speak clearly. Tell her that you need help, and why. Give her your name and tell her where you are. She'll do the rest.

Some cities have a special number to call in any emergency. If your city has one, learn it. Give your name if the police ask for it.

SOS

Anywhere, an SOS signal means "HELP!" The signal is 3 short, 3 long, 3 short. You can signal with a flashlight, a horn, a whistle, or anything else that will make the signal.

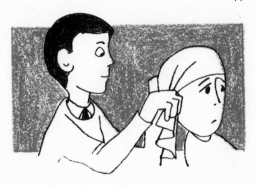

EMERGENCY FIRST AID

First Aid is for emergencies in which someone gets hurt or is suddenly ill—the things you do right away, until a doctor can treat the patient. Unless the injury is slight, First Aid does *not* take the place of a doctor's treatment.

One of the most important things about giving First Aid is that it calms the person who is hurt or sick and makes him feel that he is being taken care of. Do things carefully and quietly, and be as soothing and cheerful as you can. If you act frightened or upset, it will excite and frighten the patient, which is the last thing you want to do.

Most of the emergency First Aid measures in this book are given where we talk about the particular emergency. To find them quickly, look in the First Aid Index at the end of this section, on page 18. They are also in the index at the back of the book.

There are four emergencies in which the victim's life is in immediate danger and every second counts. If more than one of these emergencies is present, treat them in this order:

1. IF THERE IS SEVERE BLEEDING, STOP IT. You can almost always do this by pressing directly on

the wound with a thick cloth pad. This is one time when it is more important to be quick than clean. Use whatever cloth is handiest, even clothing.

Press the pad firmly, directly over the wound and hold it there until the bleeding stops. Keep pressing for at *least* 5 minutes, and use your watch or a clock — don't guess about the time. In an emergency, one minute can seem like half an hour, and if you release the pressure too soon the bleeding will start again.

If the blood is coming in spurts, it means that an artery has been cut, and bleeding from an artery can cause death in just a few minutes. Keep pressure directly over the wound *and* apply additional pressure between the wound and the heart, like this:

If blood is spurting, apply direct pressure over the wound.

Apply additional pressure between the wound and the heart.

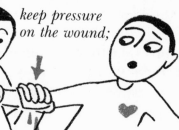

A steady flow of blood means that a vein has been cut. Apply additional pressure on the side of the wound *away* from the heart, like this:

If blood flow is steady,

keep pressure on the wound;

apply added pressure away from the heart.

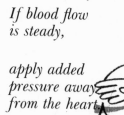

When the heavy bleeding has stopped, don't take the pad away, even if it's soaked. Bandage it firmly into place.

If the wound is on an arm or leg, elevate it with pillows or anything else that is handy, such as a rolled-up coat.

If the patient is thirsty, and the wound is not in his stomach or lower chest, give him some water — no more than half a glassful every half hour.

2. IF THE PERSON HAS STOPPED BREATH-ING, START ARTIFICIAL RESPIRATION.

It is vital to start air moving in and out of his lungs at once. The fastest way to do this is by the mouth-to-mouth method. It works like this:

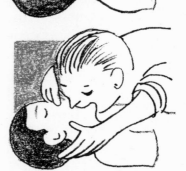

a. If you can see anything in the victim's mouth that doesn't be-long there, wipe it out with your fingers, or with a cloth wrapped around a finger.

b. Tilt his head back as far as possible. Pull the jaw into a jutting-out position.

c. Open your mouth wide and take a deep breath.

d. Seal your mouth around his and blow in, closing off his nos-trils by pressing your cheek against them. (Or pinch them closed with your fingers.)

If you'd rather, you can open a handkerchief between the victim's mouth and yours, and blow through that. He will still get air.

e. Take your mouth away, turn your head to the side and listen for the air to come rushing back.

For an adult, take 12 breaths a minute. For a child, take shallower breaths, about 20 a minute. (If the victim begins to look bulgy from too much air inside, press his belly to push the air out.)

push up

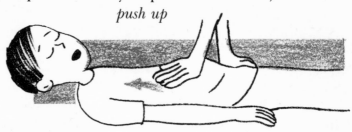

You can do this for hours if you have to. People can also take turns. Don't stop until he starts breathing by himself, or a breathing machine comes.

3. IF SOMEONE HAS SWALLOWED POISON, EITHER DILUTE IT BY MAKING HIM SWALLOW A GREAT DEAL OF MILK OR LUKEWARM WATER, OR MAKE HIM SPIT IT UP. Which treatment you use depends on the poison, so look for the poison container.

If the poison is a drug (even too much aspirin can be a poison to a small child), make him vomit it up. Sometimes just tickling the back of his throat with your finger will do it. Forcing down quantities of lukewarm water mixed with mustard usually will cause vomiting. (Any substance that causes vomiting is called an *emetic.*)

If the poison is a household product such as lye or a detergent, cleaning fluid, or turpentine, *don't* make the patient vomit. Just dilute the poison with lots of milk or water.

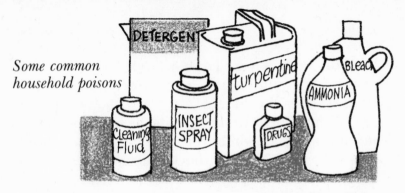

Some common household poisons

Once you've started emergency First Aid, call for help.

Many cities have Poison Emergency Centers where there are always doctors at the phone to give immediate advice. Ask the operator to connect you with the nearest center, *and* to send an ambulance. Have the container in your hand while you're calling, so you can describe the poison. Try to figure out, too, how much the person took.

4. IF SOMEONE IS BADLY BURNED, YOU MUST RELIEVE THE PAIN, PREVENT INFECTION, AND TREAT FOR SHOCK.

If the burn is from fire, boiling liquid, or hot metal, do *not* try to strip away any clothing that is sticking to the burn. (For chemical burns, see page 40.)

You relieve the pain by keeping air away from the burn. Do this by covering it loosely with a thick dressing of at least four layers of cloth (six layers are better), sterile, if possible; at least, very clean. Strips of clean, ironed sheets are fine. Then fasten the dressing loosely in place with additional layers of cloth. The thick dressings also keep the burned area clean.

Do not wet the dressing or apply any kind of grease, medication, or ointment. Do not use cotton.

If the burn is very large, wrap a clean sheet or a large towel around it and cover loosely with clothing if the weather is cold.

Get the patient to the hospital as soon as possible but, meanwhile, while you are giving emergency First Aid, treat him for shock. Shock is the greatest danger after a severe burn.

Shock

In *any* kind of accident or medical emergency, it is safe to think that the victim is suffering from shock.

Usually a person in shock is pale, perspiring, and short of breath, but don't guess—play safe. People in shock can die, even if their injuries are not great.

No matter what the accident is, the treatment for shock is always the same.

Keep the person lying down, even if he doesn't want to.

Keep his head lower than his body *unless* he has a head or chest injury. Then his head should be slightly raised.

Keep him warm, but not hot. He should have a blanket under him, if he's on the ground outside. He should have a blanket over him, wherever he is. (A person in shock loses body heat fast, which makes the shock more severe.)

If he is conscious, give him something hot to drink—tea or coffee or cocoa. But *never* try to make an unconscious person swallow anything.

covering over

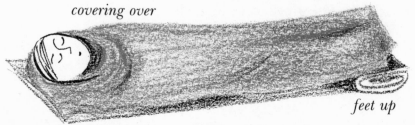

feet up

blanket underneath

Be quiet and cheerful. Don't do anything to frighten the victim. Don't talk about his injuries.

Chronic Illness

If any member of the household has a chronic illness (one that is never really cured, such as a bad heart, diabetes, epilepsy, or asthma), all members of the household should know what First Aid to give if he has an attack. (Get emergency directions from the family doctor.) Know where critical medicine is kept, and how to give it.

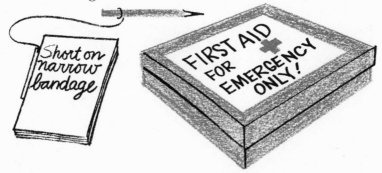

EMERGENCY FIRST AID EQUIPMENT

Every household should have this First Aid equipment, all together, in a special place, to be used only in emergencies. If you use anything, replace it at once. Even if you have some of these supplies in your family medicine chest, have them in your emergency kit, too.

An antiseptic, such as Mercurochrome or Merthiolate (iodine can cause a burn)

Adhesive bandages, several sizes

Adhesive plaster

Several rolls of gauze bandage, different widths

Sterile gauze pads, 3 x 3 inches

Needle, scissors, and tweezers
Smelling salts
An elastic bandage, 2 or 3 inches wide
Eye wash and cup
An emetic, such as syrup of ipecac
An old sheet—clean, ironed, cut in wide strips (about 8 inches), in a plastic bag to keep it clean
A triangular bandage. This can be made from the sheet, too. It should be about 55 inches at the base and 36 inches along each side
An extra supply of special medicine if anyone in the household depends on it

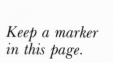

Keep a marker in this page.

EMERGENCY FIRST AID INDEX

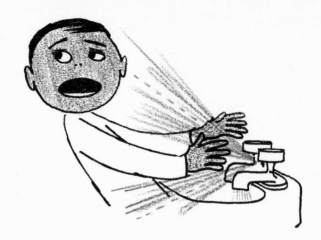

HOUSEHOLD EMERGENCIES

The more comfortable people's homes are, and the more things they have to make living easier, the more things there are to break down. Most of these breakdowns are *not* emergencies. No matter how you feel about it, it really isn't an emergency if the television set goes off. Major appliances—television sets, washing machines, stoves, refrigerators, and furnaces need professional fixers. Don't tackle them yourself.

For one thing, defective appliances are dangerous. Any electric appliance, when it is connected into the socket, can carry a tremendous electric charge. If the appliance is working all right, the electricity won't hurt you. (Be careful during an electrical storm, though—see page 81.) If something goes wrong with an electrical appliance, the safest thing to do is to turn it off and disconnect it from the wall socket. Don't connect it again until the appliance man has fixed it.

FIRST turn off the appliance;
THEN disconnect it.

Don't touch gas appliances either. If you smell gas, don't try to find the trouble yourself. Call the gas company's emergency service — the operator will get the number if you tell her it's an emergency — and someone will get there fast. There is no charge for emergency service. While you're waiting, open the windows wide.

Wherever you smell gas, in the cellar or near the stove or a gas refrigerator, *never* use a match, a candle, or any open flame. Don't turn on electric switches near the leak, either. A flame or a spark could cause any leaking gas to explode.

Water, gas, and electricity come in from outside.

KNOW YOUR HOUSE OR APARTMENT

Most houses are supplied with water, gas, and electricity from outside. Any of these can be turned off in an emergency. Everyone in the house who is old enough and responsible enough to use the information should know where the turnoffs are, and how they work. It's a very good idea to tack a card, telling where each turnoff is, on the kitchen bulletin board, or on the cellar door, or in the service area.

Most apartments have turnoff valves for individual appliances using water—sinks, toilets, etc. But they usually do not have one main turnoff valve. In an emergency, the superintendent can shut off utility service to the whole house.

Electricity

Electric current comes into a house or an apartment through the electric meter, into a fuse box or a circuit breaker box. In private houses and in some apartments the electric cutoff switch is usually on the fuse or circuit breaker box. This switch controls all the electricity coming in. When it is off, all the electricity in the house is off.

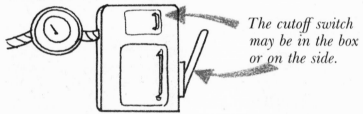

The cutoff switch may be in the box or on the side.

There are three emergencies in which all the current should be turned off:

1. If the cellar is in *danger* of flooding, turn off the current. But if the place where the main switch is located is already flooded, *don't* go near it.

2. If someone is in contact with a defective appliance or a live wire and is being shocked, turn off the current before you try to help him (see page 39).

3. The last and most likely emergency is if a fuse blows and you have to change it. *Never* change a fuse unless the current is off.

A fuse is a strip of metal between the main wire that carries (or conducts) electricity from outside your house or apartment, and the wires in the walls of your house. A fuse keeps these wires from carrying too much electricity. The fuse melts, or blows out, before the wire gets too hot. When the fuse blows, the current into those wires stops.

All houses have either a fuse box or a circuit breaker box.

Many apartments have them — usually in the kitchen or in the front hall closet.

Some smaller apartments do not have their own fuse boxes. If a fuse blows, call the superintendent.

Each fuse controls the current to one or more rooms.

Make a diagram like this:

A circuit breaker box looks like this.

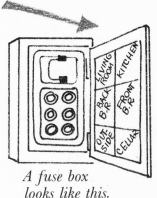

A fuse box looks like this.

showing which fuse controls the current into which rooms, and paste it inside the fuse box door. Then, if the lights go out in any part of the house you'll know which fuse to change. Every fuse is marked with the number of amperes it carries. (An ampere is a measure of electric current.) When you replace a fuse, always replace it with one of the same number. Keep a supply of the right kind of extra fuses near the fuse box.

When a fuse blows and the electricity in that part of the house goes off, it means something is wrong. Fuses don't wear out. There may be too many appliances in use on the line the fuse is guarding. Heaters, toasters, and irons, for example, need a lot of current. If they are all on the same line, they may draw too much current to be safe. Or there may be something wrong with one of the appliances which is causing a short circuit. Before you change the fuse, unplug the appliances it serves. If you don't, the new fuse may blow as soon as you turn the current back on.

Changing a Fuse
To change a fuse:
Turn off the current by pulling the electric cutoff switch to the *off* position. Be sure you have a flashlight with you!
Unscrew the fuse that blew. If you haven't got a diagram to show you which it is, the bad fuse will look like this:
(This usually means too much current in the wire.)
or this:
(This usually means a short circuit in some appliance.)

Replace it with a fuse of exactly the same amperage or number.
Pull the master switch back to *on.*

The amperage number is on the fuse.

When you change a fuse, *never* stand on a wet, or even a damp floor. Water conducts electricity. It's a good idea to keep a wooden board on the floor under the fuse box. Wood is a poor conductor.

Never change a fuse or handle anything electrical when your hands are wet.

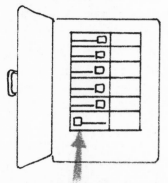

Something is wrong on this circuit.

Some houses have circuit breakers instead of fuses. A circuit breaker does the same safety job as a fuse. When there is a short circuit or an electric overload on a wire that uses a circuit breaker, a safety switch opens and the current stops. If the trouble isn't found and fixed before the circuit breaker is reset, it will just go off again.

To reset the circuit breaker, you push a button on it which closes the switch. It is not necessary to turn off the current to reset a circuit breaker.

Gas

If you use gas from tanks outside your house, the turnoffs are on the tanks.

If you use gas from the utility company, the turn-off is next to the gas meter.

You don't turn off the gas at the meter unless:
1. There is a community emergency and you receive instructions, over the radio, to turn it off. Then follow the instructions exactly.
2. You report a strong smell of gas in your house to the utilities company emergency service and they tell you to shut the main gas valve off.

If the main valve is turned off for any reason, *don't* try to turn it on yourself. Call the gas company and let them do it. There's more to it than just flipping the switch.

Water

There are two main turnoffs for the water that comes into your house. There is one in the street, which the water company uses. There is another where the main water pipe comes into the house. There are also separate turnoffs for every sink, toilet, tub, or other water appliance. Usually these shutoffs look like little wheels. Everyone should know where

they are. If there is a big leak, or a pipe breaks, or a toilet overflows, you can shut off the water to that appliance until the plumber comes. You shut it off by turning the wheel all the way to the right until the water stops.

In a plumbing emergency, shut the water off and call the plumber. Most plumbing jobs call for an expert.

Stopped-up Toilet

A stopped-up toilet is a simple plumbing emergency that usually isn't too hard to fix. You need a *plumber's friend.*
Use it like this:

If that doesn't work after a dozen or so strong strokes, try a *snake.* Use it like this:

Work snake down into the outlet.

Pump up and down hard against bowl outlet.

Locked Out

Being locked out of your house is a small emergency, and not an emergency at all if you are prepared in advance with an extra key, hidden in some special place.

If you live in a house, decide on some out-of-the-way place (NOT the mailbox or the milk box or under the mat) in which to hide the door key. Everyone who lives in the house should know where the extra key is. *Nobody* else should know. Anyone who uses it is responsible for replacing it right away.

If you live in an apartment, and you have a special lock, there probably isn't a good hiding place outside your apartment, so leave your extra key with someone in the building you can trust. The superintendent is the most likely person—and he's usually around. A neighbor may not be at home when you need her. Unless you have a special lock on your door, every apartment house superintendent has a passkey anyway.

(In case you need a locksmith, know where the nearest one is.)

Usually, if you're locked out, the simplest thing to do is to go to a friend's house, have a Coke, and wait until another member of the family comes home. But leave a note on the door saying where you are, so the first one home can call you.

If anyone in the house loses a key with an identification on it, or a pocketbook with keys in it, the locks to the house or the apartment should be changed immediately.

Don't leave a window partly open or a side door unlatched "just in case." If you can get in that way, so can anyone else.

Locked In

Getting locked into some place is much more of an emergency than getting locked out. Even if you are in no danger, there's something eerie about it. The most important thing to remember is: DON'T PANIC.

If you're locked in a building, there's probably a telephone. If you can't think of anyone to phone for help, just dial the operator, and ask her to send help. Explain why and tell her where you are. She'll do the rest.

If you accidentally get locked in a room where there is no phone, there's no need to panic either. If there are other people in the house, shout until they hear you. Or open the window and shout until you attract attention. Even if you had to stay in a room for hours or even days, you wouldn't die of thirst or starve. And even an inside room has some kind of ventilation, so you have plenty of air.

If you're accidentally locked in a closet, it's *very* important not to panic. For one thing, there's less air, and you'll feel uncomfortable sooner if you use up the air by screaming and throwing yourself about. Call and bang (a shoe is good to bang with) at intervals until someone hears you. If you know nobody else is in the house at the moment, don't waste your breath. Sit quietly on the floor until you hear someone, then start calling and banging. If the door is a thin one, try throwing your weight against it, at the side near the catch.

Things That Get Stuck

Sometimes doors aren't locked shut, just stuck.

If you don't think a sticking door can be an emergency, imagine someone stuck on the other side!

First try turning the knob and holding it to be sure the catch is out of its slot, and then throw your weight against the door, if it opens in. Be sure that the person on the other side is out of the way. If the door opens out, the person inside has to shove.

If a door catch has accidentally jammed and there is no key, you might have to take the door off the hinges. You can do this by taking out the hinge pins. Pull them up or down, bottom hinge first. If a pin sticks, knock it out with a hammer and a screwdriver, like this:

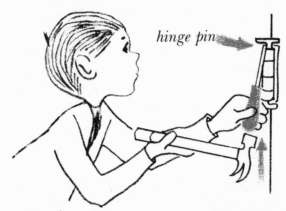

hinge pin

Then shove, whichever way the door opens. Be SURE the person on the other side is out of the way, as the whole door is likely to come off.

Sometimes parts of people or animals get stuck. It's very mysterious, but sometimes fingers get stuck in holes, hands get stuck in jars, heads get stuck between railings. They went in, but they won't come out. Almost always, making them slippery will do the trick. Cooking oil is easy to pour, and a film of oil will make most stuck things easy to pull free.

HOUSEHOLD EMERGENCIES
FOR WHICH YOU NEED THE POLICE

(DON'T try to handle any of these emergencies yourself.)

If you wake up at night and hear a prowler, *don't* try to catch him. He might be armed. If he is in another part of the house or apartment and the telephone is next to your bed, call the police or the operator. Cup your hand around the phone and speak as softly as you can.

If the prowler is in your room, lie still, observe as much as you can, and call the police as soon as you can.

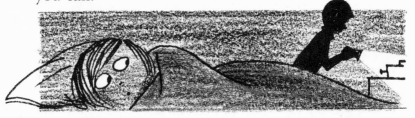

If you are threatened by a robber, do as you are told. Observe everything you can and call the police as soon as you can.

If you come home and see that the lock to the door or a window has been forced, *don't* go in. Don't touch anything. Call the police.

If you receive an obscene or frightening telephone call, *do not* answer back. Hang up immediately. If it happens several times, call the police, and notify the telephone company. The telephone company will refer your complaint to their experts who will try to trace the calls and stop them. If the police ask your cooperation in identifying the caller, don't be afraid to give it. They will protect you.

Party "crashers" can be an emergency, not just a social problem. If the uninvited guests are just one or two, and you know them personally, it's up to you whether to invite them in or not. But if there are several, and you do not know them yourself, tell them to go away and close the door immediately. If they do not leave at once, call the police.

An "open house" is a dangerous kind of party. You should always know the guests in your house. There should always be at least one male adult in the house during a party. He doesn't have to be a parent—he can be an older brother, or an uncle, or a neighbor. Adults don't have to be in the room where the party is, but all the guests should know that they are around, in case of an emergency.

Never invite an unexpected stranger into the house. If he asks to see another member of the family, let him wait outside while you get that person. If the person he asks for isn't home, tell him to come back some other time.

If a repairman is expected, or somebody is going to work in the house, those at home should know about it, and he should show some identification before he is let in.

It's not a good idea to open the door at any time
without knowing who's on the other side. If you have
a peephole, use it. If you don't, ask, "Who is it?" If
you're not satisfied with the answer, don't open the
door.

FIRST AID FOR HOUSEHOLD EMERGENCIES
Broken Bones

Except for traffic accidents, falls
at home are the commonest cause
of broken bones. The older people are, the more likely they are
to break bones when they fall.

A broken bone is called a *fracture*. There are two
kinds of fractures. A *simple fracture* is also called a
closed fracture, because it is under the surface of the
skin. If the broken bone cuts through the skin and
makes an open wound, it is called an *open*, or *compound fracture*. Most broken bones are simple fractures.

You can't always tell if a bone is broken, but it
might be if:
The person who fell says he felt the bone break;

The place is tender to the touch, with a lot of pain in one place;

The body part is out of normal shape;

It begins to swell;

It hurts to move.

Never test for a fracture by having the victim move the part, or put his weight on it. If you even *think* a bone is broken, play it safe.

First Aid: Keep the broken ends and the joints around them quiet and in a natural position. Slipping pillows under and over the injury is a good way to do this. If there is no break in the skin, an ice bag or cold, wet dressings will help keep the swelling down.

You may tie the pillows in place, but be sure the knot isn't over the injury.

If the fracture is compound, apply a dry, sterile dressing to the wound.

Control bleeding by direct pressure (see page 12).

Do not push the bone back, if it is sticking out.

Call the doctor.

Give First Aid for shock (see pages 16-17).

Sprains and Dislocations

Sprains are injuries to ligaments and muscles and blood vessels around a joint. A dislocation is the displacement of the end of a bone from its joint. Sprains and dislocations both have the same symptoms as fractures — swelling, tenderness, and pain if they are moved.

First Aid: Since you can't tell which is which at first, treat sprains and dislocations as you would a fracture. Rest the injured part on a pillow or a rolled-up blanket. Call the doctor. Apply an ice bag or cold wet dressings if there is no break in the skin.

Head Injuries

Head injuries can be caused by falls or a blow on the head, and might be very serious. If someone is knocked unconscious, call the doctor at once.

First Aid: Put a small pillow under his head. Turn his head gently to the side. Loosen clothing around his neck. Keep him covered.

Even when he regains consciousness, keep him quiet and lying down. Don't rush him off to the doctor — it's better if the doctor comes to him.

Do *not* give him any stimulants, such as whiskey.

If he has a wound on his scalp, just lay a dressing over it and bandage it in place, without jiggling him around.

A triangular bandage stays in place over a head wound.

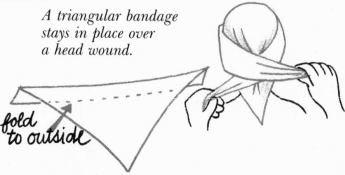

fold to outside

Fainting

People faint because their nerves suddenly cut down the blood supply to the brain. This can happen if they are frightened or surprised, shocked by some sudden news or by something they see. Some people faint if they see others hurt. Some people faint in crowds or even in stuffy rooms.

First Aid: If someone feels faint, have him lie flat if he can, with his head lower than his feet. If he is sitting, have him lower his head between his knees like this

and breathe deeply. A sniff of smelling salts is helpful.

Whenever anyone loses consciousness, keep him lying down. The color of his face tells you what else to do.

If his face is red, raise his head. (Put a pillow under it, or a rolled-up coat, or anything else that's handy.)

If his face is pale, raise his feet. (Put pillows, blankets, or anything else under his legs and feet.)
Loosen any clothing that might keep him from breathing easily, such as a tight collar, or a tie, or a tight belt.

Electric Shock

Most households have so many electric appliances and switches that mild electric shocks are easy to get. Any electric cord is dangerous if the insulation on the cord is frayed, like this:

Even a fraction of an inch of exposed wire can cause a short circuit at the switch, or the outlet, along the cord, or in the appliance. If your hands or any part of your body is wet, or if you are in contact with something metal at the same time, the chance of your getting a severe shock is much greater.

NEVER use electrical appliances or equipment if your hands or feet are wet.

First Aid: A person in direct contact with electric current becomes part of the circuit. He can't let go. *Don't touch him directly* or you are putting yourself in danger, too. If possible, quickly cut off the house current by pulling the main switch. If you can't do that, use a long wooden stick, such as a broom handle, to push him free of the wire.

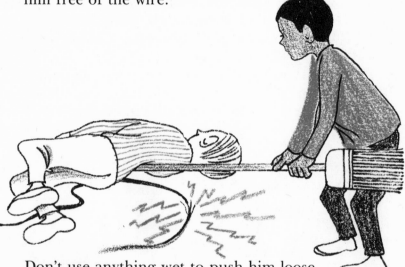

Don't use anything wet to push him loose.
Don't use a stick with sap in it.
Be sure your hands are dry, and that you are standing on a dry floor.

Once he is away from the current, give artificial respiration if the victim isn't breathing (see page 13). Even if he is stiff, he isn't necessarily dead. It may take a long time to start him breathing, so get help as soon as you can, but don't stop the rescue breathing until that help comes. If you are near a phone, it's worth a few seconds to call the operator for help. If you're not, just shout often, until someone comes; then send him for help.

Heart Attack

If someone in the family has a bad heart, everyone should know, from the doctor, what to do in case of an attack.

A first attack may be short. It may be a pain in the chest or just below, and a sharp pain down the left arm. There may be faintness and shortness of breath. *First Aid:* Do *not* alarm the patient; that's dangerous. Make him lie down, and call the doctor at once. If he feels faint, raise his feet a little, on a pillow.

If he is short of breath, raise him to a half-sitting position with pillows behind his back and head. It is more important for him to breathe easily.

Try to seem relaxed and cheerful while you're waiting for the doctor.

Chemical Burns

Many household products, such as lye, ammonia, or strong bleaches can burn the skin badly. *First Aid:* Wash the skin right away with lots of water. Then pat on diluted vinegar or lemon juice.

If the burn is from an acid, such as battery fluid, first wash with lots of water, then with soapsuds.

Check your house, then list and fix emergency makers.

PREVENTING HOUSEHOLD EMERGENCIES

Preventing emergencies is better than knowing what to do when they happen. Any of these things can cause an emergency:

Loose railings or loose steps;

Rickety chairs or ladders;

Slipping rugs;

Cracked window panes;

Frayed appliance cords;

Loose screws — on door hinges, on shelves, in furniture, on bicycles;

Closet doors with snap locks, or no inside knobs;

Empty iceboxes, or trunks that a child could crawl into;

Dark stairs and halls;

Things scattered on the stairs or on the floor;

Spilled grease or water on the floor;

Household poisons in reach of children;

Unlocked doors or ground floor windows when everyone is out, or at night;

Amateur "fixers" in the family who tinker with appliances;

Climbing on stacked chairs, boxes, or tables instead of a stepladder;

Switching electrical appliances off and on when hands — or any parts of the body — are wet or in water.

(For preventing fire emergencies at home see pages 52-53.)

CHECKLIST OF HOUSEHOLD EMERGENCY EQUIPMENT

Every household, even if it's a one-room apartment, should have these things on hand. When something is used or used up, replace it.

Enough canned food to feed every member of the household for at least two days. (Don't forget the family pets!) This should include canned fruit juice or bottled drinks to take the place of water in case you have none.

A transistor radio in working order.

A flashlight in working order. (Keep extra batteries for radio and flashlight, wrapped in plastic wrap.)

Fire extinguishers.

Candles and matches in a waterproof container.

A complete First Aid kit (see pages 17-18).

Hammer, screwdriver, pliers, different sizes of nails, friction tape, fuses, plumber's friend, and a 10-foot auger, or "snake."

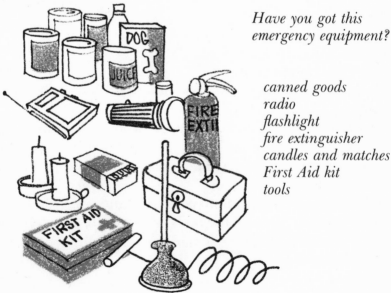

Have you got this emergency equipment?

canned goods
radio
flashlight
fire extinguisher
candles and matches
First Aid kit
tools

FIRE EMERGENCIES

If there is a fire in the house, it is more important to get all the people in the house or apartment out safely than to try first to put the fire out. In a fire, it is also more important to act calmly than to act quickly.

Have fire extinguishers handy and be sure they are in working order. They don't have to be big ones—there are several kinds that come in push-button cans. There should always be a fire extinguisher in the kitchen, where most household fires start.

Be prepared for a fire at home by knowing a way to escape from every part of the house. Whether you live in a private house or an apartment, every family should have fire drills so that everyone knows exactly what to do to get out safely. If there are babies, small children, or old people in the family, the others should be responsible for them. Everyone should know what his responsibilites are in case of a fire. Make this part of the fire drill.

If a fire starts, call the fire department right away, even for a fire as small as a wastebasket fire. If the fire is *very* small, try to put it out yourself while you are waiting, but even if it seems to be out, have the firemen check to be sure.

Never try to put out a fire that has started from a gas appliance. That's a job for the firemen.

To telephone the fire department, follow whatever local regulations your town or city has. In some places you call the operator; in some, you call the police; in some, you call the fire department directly. You should know what number to call. Speak clearly and be sure to give the address. If you live in an apartment house, give the floor and the apartment number, too.

If you live in a private house, warn everyone in the house and be sure they get out. In an apartment building, try to get everyone in your apartment out, but leave the rest to the fire department.

Leave the building yourself, *and do not go back in.* On the way out, close every door you pass through. Closed doors slow down a fire.

Once you're out,
DON'T GO BACK IN.

If you don't see the fire start but smell smoke, and don't know how big the fire is, or exactly where it is, shout out and warn everybody in the house or apartment. Keep shouting until you are sure they have all heard you. Each one takes charge of the household members he is responsible for.

Call the fire department.

Leave at once. If you can actually see flames anywhere, leave first and then call the fire department from outside.

If there are any closed doors between you and escape, feel each door with the palm of your hand before you open it. Then brace your foot against the door and open it slowly. If the door is hot, *don't* open it. The fire might be blazing fiercely right on the other side.

First, feel the door with the palm of your hand;

If it isn't hot, brace your foot against the bottom (this keeps superheated air, or fire, from rushing at you). Then open the door slowly.

If there is no other way out except through that door, stand in the window and shout to attract attention. Close the doors and transoms to the room. Open the window just enough so you have fresh air to breathe while you are waiting to be rescued.

Don't jump out of any windows above the first floor. Wait for help from below.

If you are in the building and the fire engines have already arrived, stand at the window and wave and shout until the firemen see you and can raise a ladder to the window. *Don't* push or drop anyone from a window unless there are firemen and nets waiting and ready below.

If you have to pass through a smoky room, crawl through on your hands and knees. Smoke rises, and the air is fresher near the floor.

It's a good idea to tie a handkerchief over your nose and mouth.

If your clothes catch fire, *don't run*. Running spreads the flames. Roll up in a blanket, a rug, or a coat to smother the flames.

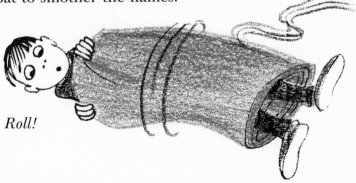

Roll!

TURNING IN AN ALARM

If you are on the street and you see smoke or flames coming out of any house, go to the nearest fire alarm box and turn in the alarm. There is always a red, blue, or orange light on the post that holds the fire alarm box. In cities, there is one on almost every corner. You should know where the fire alarm box nearest to your house is, so look for it the next time you go out. Read the instructions on it for turning in an alarm, so you won't have to stop in an actual emergency.

To turn in an alarm, just follow the directions on the box. Then wait at the box so you can tell the firemen where to go. In some cities the alarm box holds a telephone that is connected to fire headquarters. You can give the address to the fireman who answers.

Turning in a false alarm is a crime. Try to stop anyone you see who is turning in a false alarm because firemen who are answering false alarms can't be fighting real fires at the same time.

PUTTING OUT SMALL FIRES IN THE HOUSE

The best way to put out a small fire is to use a fire extinguisher. Fire extinguishers should be tested regularly to be sure they are in working order.

Putting a tight lid on a fire in a metal trash can will smother a fire in it.

A small rug, or a heavy coat or blanket, wrapped tightly, will smother a fire in someone's clothes.

You can throw a rug over a small fire and trample it out.

Plenty of water is fine for putting out a small fire, but *never* throw water on a fire in or around any electrical equipment. *Never* throw water on a fire in an electric, gasoline, or oil stove.

In any kind of stove fire, it is more important to put out the fire than to rescue the food.

FIRE IN A PUBLIC BUILDING

Whenever a large number of people are involved in a fire, there is much more chance of a panic. The panic is usually more dangerous than the fire, because it prevents people from getting out safely. If there is a fire in a public place, and people start jamming toward the main exit, look around for another way out. The law requires that all public buildings must have at least two ways out from every part of the building.

Look for another way out!

Whenever you come into a public building—a theater or a store or a sports arena—look around for an emergency way out. Doors and stairways leading to the outside have red EXIT signs over them. When the building is in use, emergency exits should *never* be locked.

Doors in all public buildings are supposed to open out. That's so a crush of people inside can't trap themselves against the door. If you notice doors in any public buildings that do not open out, report this to your local fire department.

Also report any conditions that might cause a fire, such as piles of rubbish or oil puddles.

RESCUING AND BEING RESCUED

Rescuing someone in a fire might be as simple as telling the firemen where you think someone is in a burning building. It might be keeping a sharp eye out for anyone in any window or on the roof of a building on fire.

You might rescue someone by leading him to safety if he is too young, or too old, or too frightened to take care of himself. If the person can walk, lead him, but don't let go of him, even for an instant. Don't let him go back for any reason.

The most difficult kind of rescue is getting a hurt or unconscious person out of a burning building. First, be sure his clothes are not on fire. If they even *smell* smoky, wrap him in a blanket or a coat. If you are getting an unconscious person out of a burning building, be sure to look where you are going at the same time.

You can carry a small child in your arms. You can carry a heavier one like this — it's called the fireman's carry.

fireman's carry

If you have to leave someone, look out first and count the number of floors up, and the number of windows from the corner.

If the person is so heavy that trying to move him means putting your own life in danger, leave him as close to an outside window as possible. First, look out and notice the exact position of the window so you can send the firemen in to rescue him. Then, on your way out, shut every door you pass through. It might slow the firemen down a little, but it will slow the fire down a lot, which is more important.

FIRST AID IN FIRE EMERGENCIES
Burns
For First Aid for burns, see page 15. Always treat a burned person for shock, too (see pages 16-17).

Smoke Inhalation
If the person is unconscious and breathing badly or not at all, because he has breathed too much smoke, or hasn't enough oxygen, start artificial respiration (mouth-to-mouth) as soon as possible (see pages 13-14). Continue until other help comes.

PREVENTING FIRE EMERGENCIES

Check to be sure there are no emergency makers where you live, whether it's a private house or an apartment. Any of these things can cause a fire: Matches where small children can reach them;

Careless smokers who flick hot ashes anywhere, who leave lighted cigarettes, who smoke in bed;
Frayed electrical wires on lamps and appliances;
Too many lights or appliances connected into one wall socket;

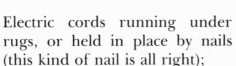

Electric cords running under rugs, or held in place by nails (this kind of nail is all right);
Appliances without an approved test label, a tag that means that they have been tested and are safe;

Lighting circuit fuses bigger than 15 amperes;

Paint cans, turpentine, cleaning fluid, or fireplace or barbecue fire-starters, stored carelessly (these should all be stored in metal cans, tightly closed, away from the heat);

Oily rags, papers, or rubbish in the basement, in the attic, or under the stairs;
A smell of gas around the stove or in the basement;
Grease accumulated in the stove;
Oil puddles in the basement or the garage;
Long flowing sleeves or long loose hair worn by anyone who is cooking;

A window curtain that could blow near the stove burners;
Things stored around the furnace, or the chimney, or the flue pipes;
Turning the furnace on in the fall without having it cleaned and checked.

Always remember, *most fires are caused by carelessness.*

*Don't answer an ad for a
sitter unless you know the
advertiser.*

SITTER EMERGENCIES

Before you even take a sitting job, be sure that the
emergency isn't you. It's a good idea to know the
people you are sitting for, or to get sitting jobs
through your school, church, or Y. But be very careful about answering an ad for a sitter that is posted
in a Laundromat, supermarket, or other public place.
Don't answer the ad unless you can find out something about the person who posted it.

Never take a car ride with a stranger to the place
where your sitting job is, or is supposed to be.

If you are a girl sitter and you're sitting at night,
one of the parents you are sitting for should see you
home, even if you live only a short distance away. If
there is only one parent, then some adult in your own
family should call for you.

Once in a while a father might try to treat you as a
girl friend, not as a sitter. Be very definite about putting him in his place, even though he is older, even if
he is a friend of the family. If you have to be rude,
be rude. *Don't* sit for the family again. Even if you're
embarrassed, or you don't want to think about it, tell
your parents what happened.

When you take a job as a sitter, you are taking the responsibility for the child or the children you are sitting for. While you are with them, they come first — before friends, telephone calls, television programs, homework, or anything else.

Go a little early, if you don't know the children, and make friends with them while their parents are still at home.

Find out *exactly* what you are supposed to do; if you are supposed to feed the children, put them to bed, change them, read to them, leave the lights on or off.

Find out where First Aid supplies are kept.

If you are taking care of them during the day, find out what they are allowed to eat and do.

Be sure you know where the parents are, and if possible have the telephone number where they can be reached.

Have the doctor's number. The number of a reliable neighbor is nice to have, too. (Be sure you find out just where the telephone is!)

In an emergency, you don't want to waste time looking for the telephone.

Ask if anyone is expected.

Do not let *anyone* in the house unless you actually know the person, no matter who he — or she — says he is, or what excuse he gives.

If *anything* goes wrong while you're in charge, be sure to tell the parents about it when they come home. If you have made a mistake, don't be ashamed to admit it. The parents will respect you for it.

Comforting is good First Aid.

SITTERS' FIRST AID
Scrapes and Scratches

Wash your own hands thoroughly with soap and clean water.

Wash the wound with soap and water.

Dry it with a clean piece of gauze.

Put on a sterile dressing — an adhesive bandage is usually enough.

Insect Bites

Calamine lotion relieves itching. You can use a paste of cold cream and baking soda instead. An ice cube is soothing rubbed on a bee or wasp sting. Bee stings, especially, are very painful. If the child is allergic to bee or wasp stings, you should know this, and what to do (see pages 99-100).

Animal Bites

If the bite breaks the skin, wash it with soap and water and call the doctor. Remember what the animal looks like, and try to find out to whom it belongs. (For more about animal bites, see pages 62-63.)

Bumps and Bruises

A light bump or bruise just calls for comforting. If the bump or bruise is heavy enough to bleed hard, hold a thick, clean cloth directly over it and press hard.

If the bleeding doesn't stop in a minute or so, call the parents. Keep holding the cloth in place.

If a bump or fall is hard enough to knock the child out, don't move him. Call the doctor and the parents right away. Then keep the child warm with a blanket until the doctor comes.

Burns

If it's a small, very light burn—just a slight redness of the skin—run cold water over it. If the burn is big, or deep, call the doctor right away; then cover it with a clean, dry cloth. Keeping air away from a burn relieves the pain (see pages 15-16).

Treat the child for shock (see pages 16-17).

Stomachache

A mild stomachache usually isn't serious. Keep the child quiet, and don't give him anything to eat (no medicine either). If he seems in real pain, call the parents.

Nosebleed

Sit the child down with his head back like this: Pinch his nostrils together like this:

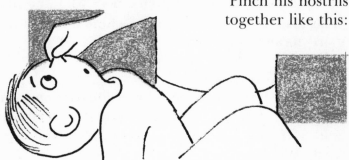

If the bleeding doesn't stop, put a cold, wet towel over his nose and face. Don't let him talk, laugh, blow his nose, or walk around. If the bleeding doesn't stop in 10 minutes, call the parents.

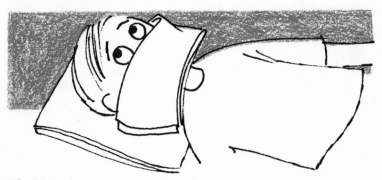

Choking

If the child starts to cough, don't try to stop him.

If he seems to be choking on something he has swallowed, pat him sharply, high on the back. If he continues to really choke, call an ambulance immediately. Don't give him anything to eat or drink. Even if the choking passes, be sure to tell the parents if you think he's swallowed anything.

Poison

If you even *think* the child has swallowed medicine or a household cleaning product, give him milk or water to drink and get in touch with the doctor and the parents right away. Hold the container while you are phoning and try to figure out how much the child took.

Keep the label for the doctor.

If you live in a large city, ask the operator to connect you with the Poison Emergency Center. They will tell you what emergency measures to take until help comes. (For more about poison, see pages 14-15.)

Convulsions

A child who is having convulsions may jerk all over with muscle spasms, or he may only twitch a little.

Put the child to bed. If he's hot, don't cover him. Call the doctor right away.

If for any reason the child stops breathing, apply artificial respiration, mouth-to-mouth (see page 13).

Splinters

If the splinter is deep, don't try to remove it. Applying Vaseline, then covering it with an adhesive bandage will make it feel less sore until the doctor can take it out.

Something in the Eye

Wash the eye with eyewash in an eyecup. If you see something—a bit of dirt or an eyelash—on the surface of the eye, see if you can lift it out with the corner of a clean handkerchief. But if it doesn't come out easily, on the first or second dab, *stop*. Call the doctor.

One dab, then stop.

PREVENTING SITTER EMERGENCIES

There are enough things to do when you're a sitter without having to cope with an emergency. You can prevent most of them.

In the kitchen, don't let the children near a hot stove, hot appliances, electric cords, matches.

If something breaks, pick up the big pieces carefully and wipe up small pieces with wet paper towels.

If you're cooking, don't leave pot handles sticking over the edge of the stove.

Pick up any pins, needles, or other sharp objects that you see and put them out of the children's reach.

Don't let the children leave toys on the stairs. Block off the stairs so that small children won't fall down them.

When a small child is out of bed, especially outdoors, keep your eye on him. Don't let him play in the street, or jump from high places.

Try to keep shoelaces tied—open shoelaces are easy to trip on.

If a child starts to run away, catch him as quickly as you can, before he can run into the street or get out of sight.

If the child is asleep, look at him every half hour or so. Be sure he's covered if it's cool, but that the covers are not loose or over his head.

GETTING IN TOUCH

No matter how careful you are, sometimes accidents happen. If an accident looks serious, or the child seems really ill, call the parents, then the doctor.

Almost every doctor has a special answering service that can reach him, or can get you another doctor if he is away.

While you're waiting, do not give any medicine unless you are told to. Stay with the child and keep him as quiet and cheerful as possible.

In an emergency you can reach the parents at the movies or the theater or a restaurant by calling the theater or restaurant, explaining the emergency, giving the person's name and asking that he be paged.

In an emergency, if you can't reach the child's parents, call your own, or any other adult you know who is close at hand. They will want to help *you* in the emergency.

ANIMAL EMERGENCIES

Probably the best rule to follow in most animal emergencies is to *call an expert*. If you see an animal that's hurt or behaving strangely; if your cat runs up a tree and can't get down; if a goose is frozen into a pond, or an animal is caught in a trap, don't go to the rescue yourself. Call your local humane society or the police. They have the proper equipment.

What would you do if you were bitten by a dog or cat? If it's your own pet or a neighbor's, and it's an accidental, playful nip that breaks the skin, treat it as you would any broken skin wound — wash it out, apply an antiseptic and an adhesive bandage. Any bite can become infected, so have a doctor look at it.

But if you are bitten by a stray dog or cat, it is very important for someone to catch it — (on a leash, if it is acting normally), or to shut it into some place, or to follow it until the animal can be caught and examined for rabies.

If the animal gets away and cannot be traced, the person who is bitten has to have a series of rabies shots, which are very painful.

It's a good rule not to try to catch or play with any stray animals.

CATCHING A PET BIRD

Here's a way that might help to catch your pet bird if it has accidentally flown out of the window.

Usually, it will stay nearby for a while — up in a tree or perched on a building. Spread a sheet on the lawn if you live in a private house or on the window-sill if you live in an apartment, and put its cage on it. Leave the door open, and fresh food and water in the cage. There's a very good chance that it will fly back in.

OTHER LOST PETS

Dogs and cats don't usually leave home (they're sensible enough to know where food and friends are!), but if yours does, try putting a dish of its favorite food at the front door.

In many places local newspapers don't charge for lost pet ads, so be sure to put one in if your pet disappears. (It's a good idea to have an extra tag on its collar with your name and address on it.)

OUTSIDE ANIMALS INSIDE

A squirrel or a chipmunk in the attic, or anywhere else inside the house, can be a real emergency because they are very destructive. If you ever see a squirrel inside, call your local humane society right away. A pair of squirrels can wreck a house.

Sometimes a bird flies in through the window and can't find its way out. You'll make it easier for the bird if you open all the windows top and bottom.

HURT ANIMALS

If you see a dog or a cat hit by a car, don't try to move it. Make some kind of barricade around it so it won't be hit again, and send somebody to call your local humane society, or the police.

If your pet gets hurt and it's only a small wound, apply the same kind of First Aid you would to any friend—wash the wound, apply an antiseptic, and cover it.

PREVENTING ANIMAL EMERGENCIES

Don't ever tease animals.

Don't walk directly behind any kicking animal, such as a horse or a donkey. If you have to come close, approach them from the front or side.

Never squeeze between any large animal, such as a horse or a cow, and a fence—you could be crushed.

Don't pick up baby animals when their parents are around. Animals will defend their young against any intruder. Be careful even with the family pets and their newborn.

Don't touch any animal that seems sick—you have no idea what disease it might be carrying. Birds can carry diseases, too.

Wash your hands after handling any animals.

Remember that *all* animals bite.

EMERGENCIES ON THE STREET AND IN PUBLIC PLACES

Someone should *always* know approximately where you are. Before you leave the house, tell someone where you're going, or leave a note. If you're going somewhere after school, say so. If you change your plans, let your family know.

Your best friend in most street emergencies is the nearest policeman.

In every city there are police signal boxes on the street. You can find them quickly by looking for the round green lights above them. There is also usually a lighted sign on the box reading "TELEPHONE TO CALL POLICE." These boxes are for patrolmen and for anyone who needs help. They are connected directly to police stations.

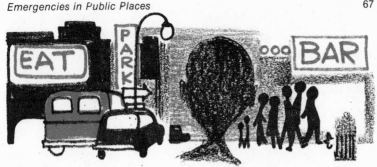

LOST

If you are lost on the street, do not ask strangers for help. Find a policeman, and he will help you find your way. If you can't find a policeman, ask for help in a drugstore or at an automobile service station. *Don't* just keep walking. You might be getting farther and farther away from any place you know. If you are in a city, you might also be getting into a neighborhood where the people speak a different language from the one you know, and won't be able to understand your questions or give directions that you can understand.

If you, or anyone you are with, gets lost or separated in a public place, such as a fairground, a department store, a railroad station, or an airport, go to the administration building or the office. Usually there is a loudspeaker and they will broadcast your name, the name of the person you are looking for, and tell the lost person where to meet you.

YOU HAVE NO MONEY

If you are away from home and you find that you have no money, find a policeman or a police station. They will let you make a telephone call, or lend you carfare home. *Never* ask strangers for money.

If you have no money, but someone says you may use the phone, you can call home collect. Get the operator and tell her you want to make a collect call. Give her the number. If you want a particular person there, give the name. She will get the number and ask if they will accept a collect call.

Never go away without money, or with only a few cents. Always keep emergency money (a dollar bill, and a dime to get the operator if you have to make an emergency call) in a special place in your wallet. If you use your emergency money, replace it as soon as you can, before you forget. Incidentally, never go anywhere without identification—a card or paper in your wallet with your name, address, and someone to call.

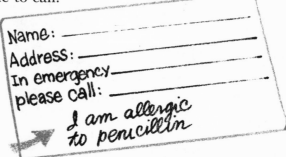

any other important information

STRANGERS

If you see a stranger loitering around your home, notify the police.

If you see a stranger loitering around school, notify the office immediately.

If a stranger asks you directions on the street, give them briefly and walk away from him. Never offer to show him the way. *Never* get into his car to show him the way. If a stranger invites you into his car, refuse, leave, but make a note of the license number and report it to the police. If you can't remember the whole number, remember the state, and as many numbers as you can, starting with the first ones.

Remember the state, any letters, then numbers.

If someone annoys you on the street, walk away, to where there are other people. Notify the first policeman you see. If the molester is persistent, or frightening, just open your mouth and scream.

Whenever you report a suspicious stranger, or a stranger who is doing something wrong, remember as many of these things as you can: The person's height, weight, age, and complexion, how he is dressed, and anything peculiar about the way he speaks or moves. Notice any special things, such as

Remember all you can about one person.

a scar, or a tattoo, or a piece of jewelry. Comparing him with someone you know will help you to remember.

If there are several people, concentrate on one. If you try to remember everything about all of them, you'll get their descriptions confused.

Unless someone needs help, mind your own business.

PREVENTING STREET EMERGENCIES
Don't speak to strangers on the street.
Don't take shortcuts, especially at night.
Don't leave your wallet in a back pocket. If you have a handbag, don't leave it flapping open.
Don't step off the curb against the light, or walk through or under construction work.
Mind your own business. Don't join in fights or arguments. But if someone needs help, get it as quickly as you can. Helping someone in trouble is everybody's business.

EMERGENCIES ON THE ROAD

When you think of a road emergency, you usually think of an accident. Everyone involved in an automobile accident, whether he is in the accident or only sees it happen, has certain responsibilities.

The driver of a car that is involved in even a slight accident is required, by law, to stop. If you are a passenger and the driver doesn't stop, remind him of this.

If possible, the cars involved in the accident must be moved off the highway immediately so other cars won't bump into them. If they can't be moved, emergency flares should be placed about 100 feet behind the cars.

If anyone has been hurt, give whatever help you can.

If the injuries are serious, don't try to move the victims. Make sure they are protected from approaching traffic. Cover them with coats or blankets

Every car should carry emergency flares.

to keep them warm. Loosen collars, ties, and belts. If anyone is bleeding, stop the bleeding (see page 11).

If you see an accident and there are no other cars at the scene, ask the driver of your car to stop and pull off the road. Then see if anyone needs medical attention.

If the ignition of a car that has been in an accident is still on, turn the key off.

Get passing drivers to warn approaching traffic in all directions. Look for a police box or send someone for police and medical assistance.

If people have been injured:

Protect them from passing traffic.

Stop bleeding.

Cover them.

Don't move them.

Remember everything you can about the accident—write it down if you can—in case you have to tell about it.

If you are in a car that is passing an accident, but other people are at the scene and helping, the driver of your car should keep going. If your car slows down, it may cause further accidents.

Don't slow down
to rubberneck.

If you are on a highway in a car that isn't working properly, the driver will get it off the highway before stopping.

These signals mean, "HELP."

Then you can signal for help by raising the hood and tying something white to the radio antenna or to the door handle on the traffic side. The first passing police car will stop, or someone will send help back. On the road, you can usually count on help from truck drivers, too.

If there is a patient in the car and you're rushing to a hospital, a white handkerchief on the antenna or the door warns other drivers that you have an emergency, and they will let your car through. You'll probably pick up a police escort, too.

GETTING IN TOUCH WITH SOMEONE ON THE HIGHWAY

In a real and desperate emergency you can reach someone who is traveling by car. Call the state police in the area, explain the emergency, and give the license number of the car and the name of the person you are trying to reach.

The license number is broadcast on the police radio, and motor police will watch for it. Sometimes the police put an emergency bulletin on the local commercial radio asking the person you are trying to reach to call in.

LOCKED OUT OF THE CAR

One of the best emergency preventers for this is an extra key, hidden somewhere out of sight outside of the car. There are magnetic holders for an extra key that can be stuck anywhere under the car. It will hold fast until it is taken off.

Sometimes car keys accidentally get locked into the trunk when someone is putting packages there. If the car itself is open, you can usually reach into the trunk to get the keys by lifting out the back seat. Otherwise, call a locksmith.

The trunk is behind the rear seat.

WEATHER EMERGENCIES IN A CAR

If you're caught in a car during a bad lightning and thunderstorm, don't worry. A metal car is one of the safest places to be. Even if lightning plays on the car itself, it will discharge into the ground; it won't jump to the people in the car.

If you're in the car during a storm and a live electric wire falls across it, *stay inside* until rescuers get the wire off. Do not touch any metal parts inside the car.

Snow and Ice

When winter storms make roads dangerous, or there is a heavy snow warning, the best place for a car is in the garage.

Never try to sit out a blizzard in a car. You can freeze to death. If you're in a car that is stalled on the road in cold weather, *don't* sit with the windows closed and the motor running. You can't smell the carbon monoxide gas that is coming into the car, but it can kill you. Always keep a window partly open.

If you are in a car that is stuck in a blizzard, leave your car if there are other cars getting through. Stop another car going in either direction and go to the nearest refuge.

If no cars come, stay in your car and, with a window partly open, run the engine for a short while until the heater warms the car. Turn it off until the car gets too cold, then start it again. This will save gas for a long wait. Listen to the radio every 15 minutes for reports. Keep the parking lights on so other cars, or emergency vehicles, can see you.

Keep a window partly open.

Keep lights on.

Get out and signal if other cars are passing. But stay close to your car.

FIRST AID FOR ROAD EMERGENCIES
Broken Bones

More bones are broken in automobile accidents than any other way. (For First Aid, see pages 34-35.)

Severe Bleeding
(see pages 11-13)

Shock
Someone who has been in an accident, even if he isn't hurt, will probably suffer from shock. Shock can be dangerous by itself, and if someone is injured, it is *very* dangerous.

Treat any person who has been in an accident for shock (see pages 16-17). Talk to him calmly and don't let him get excited.

Don't distract the driver with horseplay.

PREVENTING ROAD EMERGENCIES
Every driver should know *his* share of the rules for preventing road emergencies. But there are rules for passengers, too:

Always keep your safety belt fastened;

Don't overcrowd the car so the driver can't move freely or see clearly;

Don't distract the driver with horseplay;

Don't get out of the car on the traffic side;

Don't get out while the car is moving.

There are rules for pedestrians, too:
Don't cross against the lights, or in the middle of the block;
Don't step out from between parked cars;
If you're walking on the road, don't walk with your back to oncoming traffic;
Don't wear dark clothes if you're walking on the road at night, and if possible, carry a flashlight;

Wear something white and carry a flashlight.

Don't ask for, or accept, rides from strangers.
　　Here are some rules for bicycle riders:
Remember that bikes in the street obey the same traffic rules as cars;
If your bike is a one-seater, don't carry passengers;
Don't be a showoff—don't ride with "no hands," or frighten pedestrians for kicks.
Check your equipment. Your bell should work; there should be a light in the front and a reflector in the back; the mechanical parts should be in good shape.

WEATHER EMERGENCIES

Weather emergencies usually mean storms. Different kinds of storms cause different kinds of emergencies. Except for blizzards, most violent storms happen in hot weather.

THUNDER AND LIGHTNING STORM

Lightning can be dangerous, whether you are out in a thunderstorm or inside the house.

When you see a thunderstorm coming, if you're swimming, or in a boat, or on the beach, get out of the water or off the water, or as far away from it as you can before the storm breaks. Lightning is electricity, and water is a good conductor of electricity. (Raindrops don't count—there's too much air between them.)

Thunderheads tell you when a thunderstorm is coming.

If you are on a hill or a cliff, get down to low ground. Lightning strikes the highest thing in its path first. Tall trees and smokestacks, boat masts and flagpoles are good targets.

Don't stand under a big tree to get out of the rain. You are safer in the open. If you lie on the ground in an open place you'll be still safer, even though you'll get wetter.

If you're in the woods, it's pretty hard to get away from the trees, but find a clump of low ones and stay away from any really big trees you see. These are the ones most often hit.

If you're in the open, stay away from wires — overhead wires and even wire fences. Metal is a good conductor — that's why electric wires are made of it.

But you're perfectly all right in a car, or a train, or a plane, on a steel bridge or in a steel building. Lightning may flow through them, but it won't jump away to you. Not *all* buildings (or houses) are safe. A city building, with a steel frame, is very safe. A wooden house, with the right lightning rods, is safe, too.

But even in a safe house, it's a good idea to stay away from electrical appliances during a thunderstorm, particularly your television set. If the antenna isn't properly grounded, it can lead the lightning into your set. If the set is on, leave it on. If it's off, don't turn it on.

It's a good idea, too, to stay away from open doors and open windows (closed windows are all right) and open fireplaces. Chimneys are a good target and soot is a good conductor.

And it's a good idea to stay out of the bathtub. Most bathtubs are metal underneath their coating, and metal and water are both good conductors.

SQUALLS

Squalls are dangerous storms. They are made of a line of storms linked together, and they move so fast that they come up suddenly. A squall looks like a wall of black clouds moving across the sky.

The winds in a squall are strong, and they shift suddenly. There are torrents of rain, and sometimes hailstones. When you see a squall coming, get inside. It's particularly important to watch for squalls if you are in a small boat.

HURRICANES

Hurricanes never happen suddenly. The weather bureau starts reporting a hurricane days in advance, so pay attention if it's moving toward your area.

Usually the winds increase as the storm approaches, and may reach hurricane force (75 miles an hour or more) about six hours before the storm itself crosses the coast. A hurricane is at its worst along a coastline. Once it starts to move across land, its winds begin to lose force.

A hurricane brings three kinds of danger: 1. Tremendous winds, which can blow down trees, tear off roofs, pick up all kinds of loose objects; 2. Very heavy rains. Hurricanes are the greatest rainmakers there are. An average hurricane dumps from 5 to 10 inches of rain in a period of 24 hours. Some hurricanes dump up to 30 inches of rain; 3. The storm tide, or "surge" is the greatest danger in a hurricane. By far the largest loss of life and the greatest property damage are caused by storm tides which may be up to 20 feet higher than a normal high tide.

If there is ever a hurricane warning in your area, and you *should* happen to be alone, or the oldest family member on hand, these are the emergency measures you should take:

Before the Storm

Keep your radio on.

If you live in a low, exposed coastal area, secure the house and LEAVE for a safer place as soon as you are told to do so. If you wait too long, flooded roads, fallen trees, and power lines can block your escape. Before you go, shut off gas valves and pull the main electric switch (see page 22).

If you live away from the direct shore, away from tidal creeks or rivers, and your house is well built, stay where you are. (But *don't* stay in a small cottage, a hut, or a mobile house.)

Collect all loose objects and put them inside — trash cans, porch furniture, toys, garden tools, flowerpots.

If you have a crankdown television antenna, lower it. Remove or lash awnings and close the shutters if you have them. If you have no shutters, pull down the blinds and fasten them down to prevent glass from flying into the house. Keep a window open on the side of the house away from the wind. (This helps to equalize the air pressure in the house.) If the wind changes direction, close that window and open one on the other side.

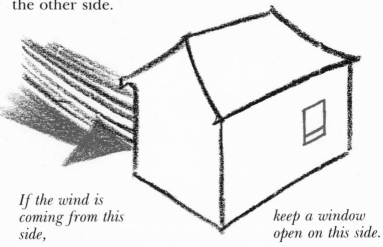

If the wind is coming from this side,   *keep a window open on this side.*

Stuff paper and rags into any openings around doors and windows.

Check First Aid supplies.

Check food supplies.

Check lantern and fuel supply and candles. Use flashlights wherever possible during the storm.

Gusts may blow candles out, or over. A flashlight is safer.

If your cellar is subject to flooding, move spoilable things upstairs.

If you have overhead power lines, prepare to lose your electric power. If your stove is electric, cook whatever food you'll need for a day or so. (Have Sterno cans and stove for reheating.)

Turn your refrigerator to the coldest setting. Even without power, food in the freezer will stay frozen for 48 hours *if* you don't open it. Open the refrigerator as little as possible to conserve cold.

Sterilize your bathtub and other containers with boiling hot water, and fill them with water for emergency use. (This is one time you don't have to worry about conserving water!) You can also use the water in the hot water heater if you need it.

Every water heater has a tap, where you can draw the water.

During the Storm

Stay inside.

Keep your radio on for weather bulletins.

Stay away from unprotected windows—they may be smashed by flying debris.

If the winds and rain suddenly stop, *don't* assume that the storm is over, even if the calm lasts for an hour or two. You may be in the "eye" of the storm—a calm place in the storm's center. If you are, the wind will start again, from the opposite direction, harder than ever. *Don't go out* until the weather bureau says the storm is over.

Even though everything looks still, DON'T GO OUT.

After the Storm

Keep the radio on and listen for bulletins. Hurricanes are famous for their uncertain paths. Sometimes they turn and come back.

When you go outside, be careful of every move. Don't touch fallen or low hanging wires of any kind under any circumstances.

Don't go near puddles with fallen wires in them.

Be on the alert for weakened tree limbs, loosened trees that might fall, undermined porches or bridges.

If you need help during or after the storm, watch for police or Red Cross disaster workers, or call them if your telephone is working.

During or after the storm, use your phone only for an emergency. Jammed switchboards prevent real emergency calls from getting through.

These are emergency calls: calls for police, firemen, doctor; reports of live electric wires; broken gas or water mains; reports of looting. Calls to friends or relatives, or to report interrupted utility service are *not* emergencies.

TORNADOES

A tornado is the most violent storm. Some tornado winds blow over 300 miles an hour. A tornado doesn't last very long—it usually passes any particular point in a minute or two. Tornadoes don't take days to form, as hurricanes do—a tornado usually forms and disappears within an hour.

Meteorologists can't predict in advance just where a tornado will strike. It turns and twists and often comes back in its own path. They do know what weather conditions are likely to form tornadoes and they can warn those areas. Tornadoes are most common over the plains and prairies. People in areas where tornadoes are common usually have storm cellars, away from their houses.

As the tornado funnel drops to the ground, it sucks up everything in its path—trees and animals and automobiles and machinery. Houses explode because of the difference in air pressure inside, and the very low pressure in the tornado outside.

The inside air bursts out, trying to equalize the pressure outside.

You can see a tornado coming.

You can hear it roaring, or buzzing as it comes close.

If you have a storm cellar, get into it.

If you have only a cellar, get into that.

Even if the place where the funnel touches the ground is quite a distance away, stay inside. The things that have been sucked up through the tornado funnel might be still whirling through the clouds spread out overhead, ready to drop.

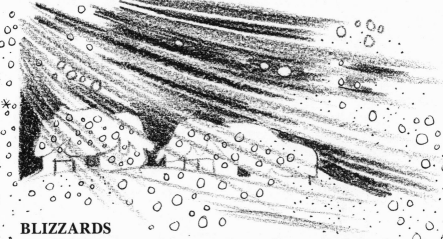

BLIZZARDS

Blizzards happen most often after a period of unusually warm weather in the winter. Weather forecasters can usually tell when a blizzard is coming. If there is a heavy snow warning or blizzard warning in your area, and you are in charge, you usually have a few hours to get ready.

Remember that you might not be able to get out for any supplies for a day or two or even more, and that no supplies will be able to get to you. You may also have to do without power.

Check your food supplies (including food for any animals you have). If you have an electric stove, cook ahead of time to get ready, in case your power goes out.

Check your fuel supply.

Check First Aid kit and essential medicines.

Do not go outside during the blizzard. Blizzard winds are very cold and strong; blizzard snows are very heavy and it is possible to get lost just a short distance away, or to get frostbitten, or to freeze.

If you live in the country, you may be completely cut off after a blizzard. But there are ways to get help if you need it.

In an area that has been hit by a blizzard, the Red Cross requests military helicopters to fly over the stricken area looking for those who need help. If you need help, make a distress signal, at least 8 feet long, out of a bright colored fabric if possible. If you have no fabric, stamp the signal out in the snow, marking it with an emergency road flare or a flag of some kind that can be seen from the air.

These are the signals that tell the helicopter what you need:

Need doctor

Need medical supplies

Need food

Need fuel

Need livestock feed

If your power fails, and you have no heat and no way of cooking, get to an emergency shelter as soon after the storm as you safely can. Bring blankets, pillows, change of clothing, and baby food if it is needed.

Be sure you have warm clothes.

(For weather emergencies in a car, see pages 75-76.)

FIRST AID FOR WEATHER EMERGENCIES
Electric Shock

After a severe storm, one of the greatest dangers is electrocution from live wires that have been knocked down. Often these wires are wet, or lying in puddles, which makes the danger even greater—you don't have to touch the wire itself, just stepping into the puddle is enough to connect you into the current.

NEVER step into a puddle where a wire has fallen.

If someone is in contact with a high tension wire, *do not touch him* or try to get him free yourself. Telephone the power company to turn off the current before anybody tries to help him.

Give artificial respiration (see pages 13-14).

Frostbite

Frostbite is the freezing of a part of the body; usually the nose, ears, cheeks, fingers, or toes. People who are exhausted, or old, or who smoke or drink a lot are more likely to be frostbitten.

If you feel a part of you getting very cold, and you can't cover it with more clothing, try to put it against a warm part of your body. If your toes and fingers feel very cold, wiggling them will help.

Hold your hand over a very cold nose.

Tuck a cold hand inside your jacket.

Wiggle your fingers and toes.

Just before frostbite occurs, the skin there may be flushed. Then it changes to a shiny white or grayish-yellow. Usually there is no pain, just cold and numbness.

First Aid: Press firmly against the part with a warm hand, *but do not rub it.* Cover the frozen part with some warm material. Get the person indoors as soon as possible, give him a warm drink, and put the frozen part of the body in lukewarm, *not hot* water, or wrap it in a warm blanket.

Be sure the water is only lukewarm.

*Keep wiggling
toes or fingers.*

Do not use a hot water bottle, a heat lamp, a stove, or radiator. If the frostbite is on fingers or toes, they should be wiggled once they are rewarmed. If blisters form, do not disturb them.

Overexposure to Cold

A person who is freezing becomes numb and very sleepy. He finds it hard to move. He staggers, he can't see well, he loses consciousness.
First Aid: If breathing has stopped, begin artificial respiration. Get him into a warm room as quickly as possible. Wrap him in warm blankets. When he is conscious, give him a hot drink.

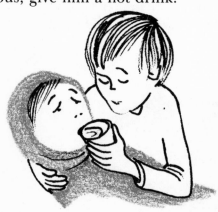

OUTDOOR EMERGENCIES

An outdoor emergency could be anything from getting stung by a bee in the park to getting lost in the woods. If you're in the park, or your own back yard, help is always close. But if you're in the woods, it might be a great distance away.

LOST IN THE WOODS

Getting lost is the most common emergency in the woods. (If you have a compass and know how to use it, you should never get lost in the woods.)

Never go into the woods without a compass, a knife, matches in a waterproof case, and a whistle. If the area is unfamiliar, you should have a map, too. Experienced woodsmen usually carry a bar of thick chocolate, in addition to whatever else they bring to eat. Don't have the chocolate for dessert—it's emergency food.

Stop.
Sit down.

The instant you think you might be lost, stop and sit down. Generally, you can't be too far away from civilization. If you panic and run, you have a tendency to go in circles.

If you have no compass, you can keep yourself going in a straight line by walking from point to point. Look ahead to a particular object you can see in the distance—a tree on a ridge, a very high rock, even a mountain—and keep walking toward it.

Keep walking toward
one thing you see in
the distance.

If you come to a river or a stream, follow it downstream—in the direction it is flowing, It will lead you somewhere.

If you see any kind of a road, or telegraph wires or poles anywhere, follow them, They will lead you to houses.

Use the sun to give you a direction.

In the morning, the sun is in the East. After noon, it is in the West.

Never walk in the woods in the dark. You might step in a hole, or get a branch in your eye. Stop *before* it gets dark, and make camp.

Build a fire, after you have cleared the ground around it of dried leaves and branches, and put stones around the fire area to keep it from spreading.

Stack enough wood alongside to keep your fire going all night if you have to. Make a bed for yourself out of pine boughs, or a big pile of dry leaves.

Keep your ears open for searchers. People are sure to be looking for you. If you hear them — and at intervals, even if you don't — use your whistle. Keep using it, but stay where you are. You're much easier to find if you're not moving around.

A whistle in the woods means, "HELP!" So does smoke. An ordinary fire isn't very smoky, so if you need help use green wood, or damp wood and leaves along with your other wood.

If you're really hungry, and your chocolate is gone, you can eat berries. Look first at the blossom end. You can eat berries with star-shaped blossom ends, like this:

Yes   *No*

Don't eat berries with round blossom ends, like this:

Sometimes you can find wild orchards in the woods.

In the spring, you can eat young ferns, if they are curled, like this:

Curled ferns look like fiddle heads.

Cattail roots don't taste very good raw, but you can eat those, too.

FIRST AID FOR OUTDOOR EMERGENCIES

Most animals will stay as far away from you as they can. The most likely bite you'll get, in the woods or outdoors anywhere, will be from a bug. Most bug bites are itchy and uncomfortable. Some are painful, and some can make you feel very sick. But even the bite of a tarantula or a black widow spider seldom kills anyone, though they are certainly real emergencies.

You can avoid most bug bite emergencies by using an insect repellent on your skin before you go into the woods, or outdoors in any buggy place.

bee   *wasp*

Bee and Wasp Stings

First Aid: Putting a piece of ice, or applying very cold water to the sting gives some relief, though bee stings can be painful for a day or two. Sometimes the whole area around the sting aches. A wasp sting swells into a hard lump, but it doesn't hurt as much or as long.

Some people are allergic to bee or wasp stings. When they are stung, they get huge hives, or their breathing is affected. This kind of allergy gets worse with each sting.

If the victim has an allergy to bee and wasp venom, use a tight band above the sting if it is on an arm or a leg, and get the person to a doctor as quickly as possible. Use ice on the sting if it's handy, but don't waste time stopping for some. It's more important to get the person to the doctor.

scorpion
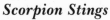

Scorpion Stings

A scorpion looks like this:
They are most common in the southwestern United States, in cool damp places. Most scorpions are not poisonous. Their sting causes swelling and feels like a wasp sting. The pain lasts about half an hour.

The sting of a more dangerous scorpion does not swell, but makes a tingling or burning feeling, followed by fever, nausea, and cramps.

First Aid: 1. If the sting is on a finger or toe, arm or leg, apply a *tight* band above the sting, toward the heart. Remove the band after 5 minutes.

band

sting

Be SURE you release the band after 5 minutes.

2. Pack the area in ice for two hours. Keep the affected part lower than the rest of the body. If the sting is on another part of the body, the ice pack is the only First Aid you can use.

3. Cover the person enough to keep him comfortable.

4. Get him to a doctor.

*reddish, hourglass
mark*

Black Widow Bites

A black widow spider looks like this:
They are common in the South, but are found occasionally in the North too. They are found in damp places inside, and outside under stones, in stumps, and in other protected places. The bite looks red, but doesn't swell much. There is pain all over the body, and cramps are severe. It may be hard to breathe or speak. The patient sweats a lot.

First Aid: The same as for a scorpion sting. If it is not possible to get the victim to a doctor at once, hot, wet applications or a hot bath may relieve the muscle cramps.

Snakebites

There are four kinds of poisonous snakes in the United States.

These are rattlesnakes. Different kinds of rattlesnakes are found all over the country. They are the most common poisonous snakes.

*Diamondback
Rattlesnake*

*Pigmy
Rattlesnake*

*grayish, with brown,
light-bordered
diamonds*

*Yellowish-gray with
dark blotches*

Copperhead

golden-brown with red-brown spots

This is a copperhead. It is found from the East Coast to the Mississippi River and across the southern United States to Texas.

Water Moccasin

brown with darker brown crossbands

This is a water moccasin. It is found in the southeastern United States and the Mississippi Valley, west to central Texas.

Coral Snake

red with black and yellow stripes

This is a coral snake. It is found along the coast from North Carolina south, westward to Texas, and in the southern Mississippi Valley.

Some parts of the country have very few poisonous snakes, some have a lot. If you are in snake country, wear boots. Anywhere, watch where you step, sit, or put your hands. Snakes won't bother you unless you disturb them.

A rattlesnake cannot strike more than a couple of feet from where it is coiled, so just step a few feet away if you see one.

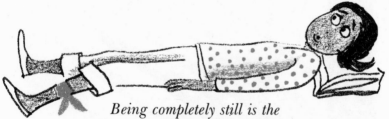

Being completely still is the most important thing.

(Don't forget to release the band in 5 minutes.)

First Aid: 1. *Don't panic.* The best thing the victim can do is to stay *completely still.*

2. Tie a constricting band firmly above the bite if it's on an arm or leg, foot, or finger.

3. Get medical care. If the patient must be moved, keep him lying down, with the injured part lower than the rest of the body. *It is more important for the victim not to move for the first hour than it is to rush him to a doctor.*

Do *not* give any stimulating drinks. Whiskey is not a cure for snakebite, in spite of all the jokes about it.

3 shiny leaves

poison ivy

Your outdoor life will be happier if you learn to recognize these plants.

poison oak

3 leaves

poison sumac

FIRE IN THE WOODS OR FIELDS

Most fires in the woods are caused by careless people. A few are caused by lightning. Fire in the woods, especially in a dry season, moves very fast, because everything in its path is fuel.

Never make a fire in the woods, or fields, or outdoors anywhere on a windy day. In many towns and cities *all* outdoor fires are forbidden.

Never throw away a match without breaking it in half, and holding it to be sure it's cold.

Never make a campfire without clearing the ground around it of leaves and twigs, *and* making a ring of stones around the fire.

Never leave a campfire burning. Douse it with water, then shovel dirt on it.

Drown it. Then bury it.

Even one burning leaf can start a forest fire. If a fire starts, douse it with water. Then trample the ground, or beat it with a shovel. Cover it with dirt. Dig and look, to be sure it's out. When the woods are very dry, the fire can burn along under the surface.

If you can't manage to put it out, leave at once and report the fire from the nearest possible place. You may not like admitting the responsibility, but it's not as bad as being responsible for losing a whole forest, with its animal life and perhaps human life, too.

If you're trying to get away from a forest fire, go in the opposite direction to which the wind is blowing. If the wind is blowing this way

go this way.

Go downhill, never uphill. Heat rises and kindles the wood above it. Fire creates an updraft, so the wind won't be blowing downhill.

WATER-SPORT EMERGENCIES

Almost all real water-sport emergencies are concerned with drowning.

Nobody who doesn't know how to swim should go in the water much above his knees.

You have to *learn* how to swim. People do not swim naturally. If you were thrown or pushed into the water, and you didn't know how to swim, you would probably do all the wrong things in trying to stay afloat.

THE BEACH

You could say that a beach — or a shore — is any place where the land meets the water. It could be the edge of the sea, or a lake shore, or a riverbank, or the side of a pool. Some of these places are safer than others. If you're in a pool, you're never very far from dry land, or a helping hand. If you're in the ocean, you can be too far from land before you realize it, and waves and currents can carry you still farther out. Be realistic about your swimming ability and don't venture where you can't get back to a feet-on-the-ground position safely and easily.

The most important rule in any emergency in the water is: *don't panic!* You will need your wits, skill, and coordination, and panic destroys them all.

Currents

If you are caught in a current that carries you with it, the most important thing to remember is *don't "buck" the current.* A strong current runs at a speed of from 4 to 6 miles an hour, sometimes more. A strong swimmer swims at a speed of less than 3 miles an hour.

If you're ever caught in a current, swim diagonally across the current, in the direction it is flowing, like this:

Even though this brings you to land some distance away, you can always walk back, or wait on dry land until someone comes for you.

If the current is directly out to sea, drift with it, shout, and wave an arm to get help from shore.

An undertow is different from other currents, as it pulls you down as well as out. But undertows don't usually go very far. If you're caught in an undertow, turn, go with it, and take a diagonal path to the surface, like this:

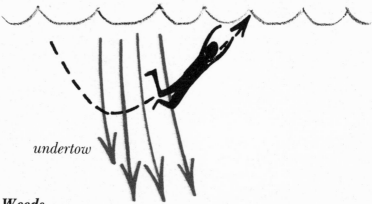

undertow

Weeds

Weeds are common in many swimming places. If you're swimming or skin diving in an unfamiliar place, ask before you dive in. If you're caught underwater in the weeds, *don't* thrash around or jerk your arms and legs. This will get you more tangled up. Move gently. See what's holding you, and unwrap it carefully. If there's a current, go with it. The current unloosens and straightens the weeds.

Cramp

Cramps make muscles knot up so tightly that they can't be used. Cold or tired muscles in your feet, your legs, or your hands are most likely to cramp up. Take a deep breath, roll to this position under the water,

and knead the cramped place hard until the circulation comes back.

If you get a stomach cramp, you can't help yourself, except by calling for help. The pain of stomach cramps makes a swimmer double up, and he cannot control his movements or his breathing.

Falling in with Your Clothes On

If you are ever thrown, or fall into the water with your clothes on, it's important to get most of them off at once. Water-soaked clothes are so heavy they will drag you down, exhaust you, and keep you from swimming.

Start with your shoes. Take a deep breath, hold it, float to this position,

and take your shoes off. (This may take several breaths if they are laced.)

Take off your skirt or pants the same way.

If your shirt, sweater, dress, or coat has to be lifted off over your head, grab it this way, with your arms crossed,

submerge and pull it over your head. Be sure it's well bunched up so it doesn't stick around your face. When your head and body are free, pull your arms out of the sleeves and swim clear.

RESCUING

If you see someone in trouble in the water, plunging in to the rescue before you think isn't very bright. Most drowning people are in a panic, which makes a swimming rescue dangerous to the rescuer. A person who is drowning can't think, or reason, or obey directions. Only someone trained in lifesaving should attempt a swimming rescue of a drowning person.

Most drownings occur close to shore. Usually you can help without putting yourself in danger, too. You can help by reaching. If the person is too far away for you to reach out and grab, you can help by extending your reach.

Here are some of the ways to rescue someone without jumping in yourself.

Sometimes you can make a wading rescue. If you do, be very sure of your footing. It's a very good idea to have something — or someone — on dry land to hold on to. This is one way.

This is another.
Try not to let the person you are rescuing grab you. Either hold something for him to grab, or grab him — by his trunks, or his hair or anything else.

BEING RESCUED

If you even *think* you're going to be in trouble while you are swimming, call for help before you get too tired or start to panic. Once you're in real trouble, you stop thinking clearly.

Don't try to swim hard or fight the current. Float or tread water slowly to save your strength. Keep your eyes on the one who is trying to help you, so you can grasp or catch whatever he throws you to pull you in or keep you floating until help can reach you.

If someone is making a swimming rescue, don't grab him, no matter how frightened you are or how glad you are to see him. Let him take hold of you. If he asks you to hold him, put your hands on his shoulders, never any place else.

AVOIDING WATER-SPORT EMERGENCIES

There should always be somebody with you when you are in the water. Even Navy divers use this "buddy" system.

Don't swim right after you have eaten. An hour is considered a safe time to wait. Stomach cramps seem to be directly connected with swimming after meals.

Unless you are an exceptionally strong swimmer, *and* are completely familiar with the tides, currents, and undertows of a particular stretch of beach, never swim or surfboard where there is no lifeguard.

Don't swim, surf, or water-ski when you are tired. Tired muscles are much more likely to cramp, especially if the water is cold.

Don't ever dive, or jump, into unfamiliar water. There could be rocks or submerged pilings, weeds, or a strong undertow.

Don't roughhouse at the edge of a pool, or show off on a diving board or on water skis. Falling and hitting your head on the way into deep water is a fast way to drown.

Don't surf where the surf is *really* big unless you are experienced.

BOAT EMERGENCIES

A person who does not know how to swim should not be in a boat at any time without wearing a life preserver.

No one should run a boat, no matter how small it is, or where it is, without knowing *exactly* what he is doing, whether the boat is a motorboat, a sailboat, a rowboat, or a canoe. He should know what the boat can and can't do. He should know the water he is boating in. He should know the "rules of the road."

The captain is the person who runs the boat. He gives the orders, and his passengers are supposed to obey. The captain is responsible for the boat and his passengers. He should be sure his boat carries the necessary emergency equipment.

The captain is responsible for the safety of his passengers.

CHECKLIST OF BOAT EQUIPMENT

An approved life preserver for every passenger.
(Non-swimmers should be wearing theirs.)
A fire extinguisher if your boat has a motor
Docking lines and a spare coil of rope
Anchor and line
A flashlight with good batteries
Oars or paddles
First Aid kit
Pump or bailer
Horn or whistle
A compass
A chart of the area
Drinking water
Extra fuel in a safety tank if it's a motorboat

EMERGENCY!

If you're ever in a boat and you need help, use any
of these distress signals:
A constant horn, bell, or whistle;
Someone waving a flag, a shirt, or anything else;
A flag flying upside down;
A white cloth flying from a mast;

Smoke or a flare;
A light blinking SOS—3 short, 3 long, 3 short;
The emergency word, "MAYDAY."

If your boat swamps or turns over, the most important thing to remember is: *Stay with the boat.*

Any boat in good condition will float and hold you up, even if it has turned over or filled with water. Even if you have only a few inches to hold on to, stay with it.

Don't try to swim for shore—it's always farther than it looks.

STAY WITH THE BOAT!

Follow this emergency procedure. Do one thing at a time.

1. Be sure that everyone is accounted for. If someone is missing, the best swimmer, holding on to the boat, or to a line, should look under the boat for him.
2. Make sure everyone has a place to hold on.
3. Catch the life preservers if they are floating, or go under the boat if they are there. Someone holds on to the person who goes under.
4. Be sure that everyone puts on a life preserver.
5. Look for whatever lines are within reach, and fasten everyone to the boat.
6. Signal for help. You should *never* be out in a small boat where, or when, rescue isn't close at hand.
7. Keep calm when you are being rescued. See that those who need help are rescued first.

RESCUING

If you are in a boat, and you are rescuing people in the water, don't put yourself in danger.

1. While you're going to the rescue, attach life preservers to lines.

2. Don't take your eyes off the people in the water.

3. Come alongside slowly.

4. Put your motor in neutral, but *don't stop it.*

5. Help those who seem tired or in trouble first. Throw a life preserver, tied to a line, and pull the person over the bow or stern of the boat. (Pulling him over the side might turn your boat over, too.)

6. Don't overload your boat. Take aboard those who need help most, and tow the others behind on life preservers, fastened to lines.

BEACH AND BOAT FIRST AID
Drowning

Even a person who seems drowned is not necessarily dead just because he isn't breathing. But it's important to help him start breathing again right away.

Don't waste a minute. Start even while he is being pulled into the boat or onto the beach. Don't stop to drain the water out.

Mouth-to-mouth respiration is the fastest kind of rescue breathing (see pages 13-14).

Exhaustion and Shock

Even if someone who has almost drowned is conscious and still breathing when he's brought ashore, he's bound to be exhausted from trying to stay afloat, and terribly frightened and in shock. Do not let him stand or try to walk.

Make him lie down, with his head lower than his feet. Wrap him in blankets or coats or whatever else will keep his body heat in.

Talk to him cheerfully and soothingly.

Give him plain water, a few sips at a time, if he is conscious.

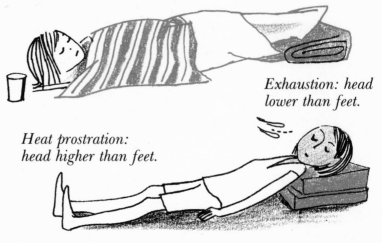

Exhaustion: head lower than feet.

Heat prostration: head higher than feet.

Heat Prostration

Too much sun and heat, on a beach, in the water, or aboard a boat, can cause heat prostration. Anyone suffering from heat prostration gets dizzy and very red in the face.

First Aid: Make him lie down with his head higher than his feet. Loosen his clothing and splash cool water on his face.

Sunburn

Don't spend a whole sunny day or even several hours in a bathing suit on a beach or on a boat unless you are very brown. Limit your time for the first two or three days. Because it is reflected, the sun is much more powerful on or near the water. Apply a suntan preparation often, especially after you've been in the water. The fairer your skin is the more protection it needs. If you're sunburned, don't get chilled.

Jellyfish or Man-of-War Stings

Some jellyfish and man-of-war stings are severe enough to cause great pain, and occasionally shock. If there are a lot of them in the water at the beach, don't go in.

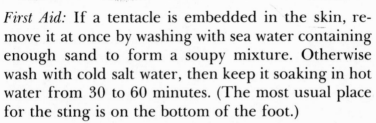

When there are lots of jellyfish in the water, be careful on the beach, too.

First Aid: If a tentacle is embedded in the skin, remove it at once by washing with sea water containing enough sand to form a soupy mixture. Otherwise wash with cold salt water, then keep it soaking in hot water from 30 to 60 minutes. (The most usual place for the sting is on the bottom of the foot.)

Meanwhile, treat for shock (see pages 16-17).

Fishhooks

If you are fishing from a beach, or a dock, or a boat, be careful of flying fishhooks. If someone gets hooked in past the barb, you can't pull the hook out the way it went in. The barb was made that way to keep the fish from pulling loose. Get the patient to a doctor as fast as you can.

GETTING IN TOUCH

If you have to get in touch with someone on a boat in an emergency, you can call the nearest Coast Guard Station, or the local Harbor Police, give them the description of the boat and its license number, and ask them to find it. (Every powerboat bigger than a rowboat has a number. So do sailboats if they have any kind of motor, even an outboard.)

If the boat is a big one, with a radio phone, you can reach the people on board by calling the Marine Operator, and giving the name of the boat. The operator will call until someone aboard answers. (You reach the Marine Operator by calling your local operator and saying, "May I have the Marine Operator?"

waterline

PREVENTING BOAT EMERGENCIES

Any boat can carry only a certain amount of weight safely. Don't overload. The waterline should not be under water.

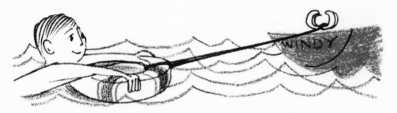

Don't ever swim from a boat without tying an emergency lifeline out behind it. If the current is strong, this gives you something to grab.

Never go out in bad weather, or without checking the weather report. Thunderstorms, squalls, and rough water are dangerous if you're in a small boat. Besides, in bad weather, there are no other boats around to help you if you get into trouble.

Never water-ski unless there are at least two people in the boat besides the skier. The driver needs to give his attention to the boat. The observer's job is to watch the skier, pass his signals to the driver, and tell the driver if he falls.

Never go out in any boat without the equipment you would need in an emergency.

WINTER-SPORT EMERGENCIES
ICE SKATING

When you're skating, wear warm, comfortable clothes. Be sure your gloves are warm enough so your fingers won't get frostbitten. Be sure your skates are not *so* tightly laced that there isn't proper circulation in your feet. Poor circulation is a cause of frostbite.

Skate only where the ice has been tested. This is particularly important at the beginning or end of the winter. Remember that brackish water is much slower to freeze than completely fresh water.

Tidal ponds are dangerous, even if the ice is thick. When the tide is out, there is an air space under the ice, and it is much more likely to cave in.

If You Fall Through the Ice

Do not try to climb out immediately.

First, kick your feet to the surface, behind you, to avoid a sitting position, which might bring your legs up in front of you, under the ice.

You CAN'T climb out from this position.

Don't try to scramble out by pressing down on the ice at the edge of the hole—the chances are that it will break again and you will take another plunge.

Extend your hands and arms forward, across the edge to unbroken ice,

kick

kick your feet back to an extended swimming position, and work your way forward, squirming across the ice.

squirm

If it breaks again, keep the same position and slide forward again. Once you are out of the water, squirm or roll away from the broken place.

roll

Rescuing a Skater Who Has Fallen Through

Never allow a crowd to collect on the ice near where a rescue is taking place.

There are a number of ways to rescue a skater who has fallen through the ice, but the most important thing to remember is: distribute the weight of the rescuers over as much of the ice area as possible, especially near the hole.

Here's a good rescue method. The rescuers lie flat, forming a human chain, each holding on to the skates of the person in front of him, like this:

Another way is to extend a long stick, a plank, or a ladder for the skater to grab. Then pull him out.

Another way is to toss a rope, weighted and looped at the end, which the skater can loop under his armpits.

However the rescue is made, the skater should always assume the extended swimming position before the pulling begins.

Exposure

First Aid: Even if artificial respiration is needed (see page 13), this is one time when it's worth a few extra seconds to get the victim inside first. But if no immediate shelter is handy, every possible effort must be made to keep him warm during rescue breathing. Put overcoats, sweaters, and blankets under and over the victim. Rub his hands and arms and legs to help restore circulation. A fire is helpful.

As soon as possible, move the victim inside. Even if he is breathing normally, even if he seems recovered, he should be taken to a doctor.

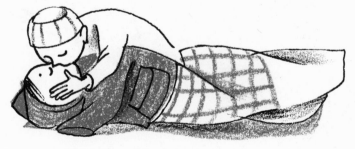

Keep the victim warm.

SKIING

Most skiing accidents happen because the skier is not skiing under control. *Never* ski on a hill or a trail beyond your skill. You should be in complete control all the time.

Never ski alone.

Never ski when you are tired. That "one last trip" up the tow and down the mountain is a poor idea.

Keep your equipment in good condition. Be sure your safety bindings are adjusted, and that your skis are fastened to your boots with a safety strap. (A released ski, hurtling down the mountain, is very dangerous to other skiers.)

The most common skiing injuries are sprains (see page 36) and fractures (see pages 34-35).

If someone is injured on the slope, do not try to move him. Build a barricade of skis and poles above him on the slope, like this. Take off his skis.

Send another skier to the base for the ski patrol. They will come with a toboggan stretcher to move him to the First Aid center.

If you are skiing cross-country, and there is no ski patrol, you can improvise a stretcher out of skis, like this:

SLEDDING, BOBSLEDDING, TOBOGGANING

The most important thing to remember, especially on a bobsled or a toboggan, is not to get going so fast that you're out of control. Sled only on clear slopes, without obstructions, such as trees or poles, or fences.

Even on an ordinary sled, remember that it is almost impossible for people to get out of your way in time if you're coming right at them. On a neighborhood sledding hill, one part of the slope should be for coming down, one for walking back up.

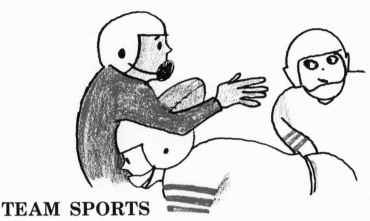

TEAM SPORTS

Most team-sport emergencies (if you don't count your favorite team losing a big game) have to do with accidents and injuries. That's why it's better to play team games under supervision, especially contact sports.

No contact sports should be played without the proper protective equipment—headgear, pads, and guards.

People simply crashing together while they are playing can hurt each other. Bats, balls, sticks, pucks, skates, and cleats are all dangerous weapons if the game gets rough.

If you ever have an accident while playing, particularly if you are knocked out, even for an instant, *don't* keep playing. Rest, while someone gets a doctor. If you are well enough to get to the doctor yourself, have someone take you there, in a car. *Don't* try to walk or bike.

The most likely injuries from team or contact sports are:

Sprains and dislocations (see page 36);

Fractures (see pages 34-35);

Being knocked unconscious (see page 57).

It's emergency-making to play hockey or baseball on a city street, other than a play street. You're likely to be part of a traffic accident, too.

HORSEBACK RIDING

Some people have the idea that all there is to riding a horse is sitting there and holding the reins. It's true that most of the horses an inexperienced rider can rent in a stable are tame and tired. Riding them is like sitting in a rocking chair. But sometimes you may get another kind of horse. And once in a while, even a tame and tired horse feels skittish or gets frightened. Then you have an emergency on your hands.

If a horse starts to run, just pulling on the reins and yelling "whoa" doesn't mean a thing to him. Most horses for hire have very tough mouths, and hardly feel a strong pull. Grab the reins up short and *jerk hard*, first on one rein and then the other. If

Grab the reins short and see-saw them.

that doesn't stop him, pull hard on one rein (make it as short as you can) so he has to go in a circle. He can't run very far that way.

If the horse rears (stands up on his hind legs), shorten the reins as far as you can and pull his head *down*.

If the horse rears,
pull his head DOWN.

If he bucks (stands on his front legs and kicks with his back legs), pull his head *up*.

If the horse bucks,
pull his head UP.

PREVENTING RIDING EMERGENCIES

Experienced riders know that they must be alert every minute.

If you rent a horse, and the stableman asks you how good a rider you are, don't brag, even a little. If you do, you're likely to get a horse that is more than you can handle. Even experienced riders don't over-estimate their abilities.

If you have to ride your horse through traffic to get to a bridle path, don't ignore traffic lights and signals. Don't show off when you're riding, and don't try to get the horse into a gallop. If you're an inexperienced rider, you are not in control if your horse is galloping. A canter should be your fastest gait. Besides, on most city bridle paths, galloping is against the law. You might get a speeding ticket!

After a canter, let your horse walk until he cools down. No good rider works his horse into a lather. And if you get him too tired, he might stumble and fall with you.

In the stable, don't ever walk around directly behind the horse. Horses kick at anything moving close behind them. Remember to keep your palm flat, like this, if you're giving the horse a treat. To a horse, a curled over finger doesn't look very different from a lump of sugar.

COMMUNITY EMERGENCIES

When a whole community has an emergency, it's usually because of some kind of natural disaster—a hurricane or a flood, an earthquake, a tornado, a forest fire. Sometimes the disaster is man-made—a fire, an explosion, a giant wreck.

Before, or during a community disaster, there are definite rules for you to follow. Keep your radio on and follow whatever *official* orders are given and no other kind. Don't spread rumors.

Don't use the telephone except in an emergency. Jamming telephone lines keeps real emergency calls from getting through.

If help is asked, give it. Bring food, clothing, or blankets to emergency stations if they are needed. Volunteer your services if they are needed. But stay off the street unless you are told to leave your house.

Do not go sightseeing to the place of the disaster. You will be in the way of emergency equipment and rescue operations.

If you live in a private house, and you are not told to evacuate during a natural emergency, here are some rules to follow:

For Gas

Don't shut off the gas at the meter unless you are told, officially, to do so.

Don't shut off the gas furnace or the water heater. *Do* turn off individual gas appliances such as the stove or the dryer.

If you have shut off the gas at the meter, *don't* try to turn it on again yourself. Wait for the gas company.

For Water

Don't shut off the main water valve unless the pipes are broken. You may need the water.

Don't draw large amounts of water for "emergency" use unless the disaster is a flood or a hurricane (see page 85). Drawing large amounts of water reduces the water pressure that the fire department might need to fight fires. If you have to, you can use the water in the water heater for drinking or cooking.

For Electricity

Don't pull the main electric switch unless there is danger of flooding.

Do shut off any individual appliances you are not using. If the power goes off, *don't* try to replace fuses or reset circuit breakers. Wait for the utility company.

Don't touch any fallen or exposed wires. If you live in an apartment, you don't have as many things to think about, because the main shutoffs are in the basement, and are the superintendent's job. But *do* turn off gas and electric appliances when they are not in use.

If the power goes off, *don't* try to replace fuses.

If you live in an elevator apartment house, and it's a long way down (and up), use your supplies sparingly. It will be quite a job to replace them if the power goes off and the elevator stops running.

EVACUATING

If you are told to evacuate, what would you take with you? Some time you may have to decide in 15 minutes, or even 5 minutes, what, of everything you own, to take.

It's a good idea to think about this ahead of time, because if you have to make up your mind suddenly you're not likely to be very sensible about it. Ask the other people in the household, too, and then write everything down. If you have a list, you can get the things on the list together very quickly, without having to think about it, and without forgetting anything.

Here are some suggestions:

If there are important papers in the house, they should be kept together, in a metal box—one that closes securely—with a handle. In the box should be:

Birth certificates.

Marriage certificate.

Social security cards or numbers.

Bankbooks.

Passports, if you have any.

Proof of citizenship if someone wasn't born in this country.

Medical records and important prescriptions, including eyeglass prescriptions.

Professional credentials.

Safe deposit key, if you have a box.

Insurance policies.

Deed, if you own your home.

(If these things are all together, it's easy to simply pick up the box if you're the one in charge.)

If anyone in the house really depends on some medicine, or on eyeglasses, be sure to take those.

Important written material that someone is working on.

A valuable coin or stamp collection.

Money, and a checkbook if you have one.

If there is an infant in the house, his formula.

Wear warm, comfortable, everyday clothes and shoes and take a jacket or a coat.

If you have time to pack a small bag, take toilet articles and a change of underwear.

If you're going to a shelter, take a pillow and a blanket, a Thermos of water, enough food for a day, and a transistor radio, if you have room.

AFTER THE EMERGENCY

You can think of any emergency as a problem, but whatever it is, you can be pretty sure that someone else has had the problem before. That's what makes it possible to have rules for particular emergencies. That's how you can be prepared. The astronauts even have plans for handling emergencies that have never happened to anyone, because they know the things that *might* happen.

Maybe your emergency is only a little one, such as getting back your pet bird after he's flown away.

Maybe it's a funny emergency, such as getting your hand stuck in the pickle jar.

Maybe it's a big emergency, in which someone's life depends on you.

After the emergency is over, it's a good feeling to know that you did the right thing.

INDEX

Accidents, automobile, *see* road
emergencies
acid burns, 40
alarm, fire, how to report, 47
ambulance, sending for, 10
amperes, 23
animal bites, *see* bites
animal emergencies, 62-65;
bites, 57;
on horseback, 131-133;
hurt animals, 65;
lost pets, 63-64;
preventing, 65;
stuck pets, 31;
wild animals indoors, 64
appliances, electrical:
defective, 20;
as fire hazards, 52
artificial respiration, 13-14;
after drowning, 117;
after electric shock, 39;
after exposure, 94;
after smoke inhalation, 51

aspirin, overdose, 14
auger, *see* plumbing
automobile accidents, *see* road
emergencies

Babysitting emergencies, *see* sitter emergencies
bandaging:
for bleeding, 13;
for head injuries, 36
basement, fire hazards in, 53
bee stings, 99
berries, edible, 98
bicycles, rules for, 78
birds, lost, 63
bites:
animal, 57, 62-65;
black widow spider, 101;
insect, 56;
snake, 101-103;
see also stings
black widow spider bites, 101
bleeding:
from an artery, 12;

139

Date Due

DE 15 70			